Contents

is book is to be returned

Basic Maths and English

AAT

Workbook

New in this edition

■ A new chapter on computer functions

BPP
PROFESSIONAL EDUCATION

First edition September 2002
Third edition September 2004

ISBN 0 7517 1729 0 (previous edition 0 7517 1228 0)

British Library Cataloguing-in-Publication Data
A catalogue record for this book
is available from the British Library

Published by

BPP Professional Education
Aldine House, Aldine Place
London W12 8AW

www.bpp.com

Printed in Great Britain by W M Print
45-47 Frederick Street
Walsall, West Midlands
WS2 9NE

chapter 1

Introduction

Many students start to learn accountancy with only a very basic understanding of maths.

This book aims to cover the basic maths skills needed at AAT Foundation Level. However it will also be useful for other students who need to brush up their maths skills.

In addition, there is a chapter on writing business English. This includes a guide to common mistakes, punctuation and spelling.

Finally this edition includes a chapter on computers, including codes, processing data and integrated systems and databases.

IMPORTANT!

This is a very basic book aimed at students who do not have Maths GCSE. Students needing higher level help, especially those at AAT Intermediate and Technician level who are intending to go on to ACCA and CIMA, are advised to obtain BPP's Business Maths and English (ISBN 0 7517 1580 8) published in June 2004.

chapter 2

Numbers
are fun

Contents

1 Introduction

This chapter deals with the basic building blocks of mathematics, how to use numbers.

We look at numbers and the skills of adding, subtracting, multiplying and dividing them.

In the final section, we will use these techniques in some number games.

2 Numbers

Numbers are important in life. Without a knowledge of numbers, how can you be sure that you get the right change when you buy something?

Numbers can be positive or negative, eg –5, –4, –3, –2, –1, 0, 1, 2, 3, 4, 5.

Negative numbers can be written as –5 or (5).

3 Addition

Most people can add small amounts together. If you have two oranges and then are given another, you have three oranges. In maths, this is shown as 2 + 1 = 3.

However large numbers can be intimidating. What is 15,267 + 27,321?

The way of dealing with this, is to write the numbers one above the other. The columns then represent multiples of ten, so 27, 321 becomes:

10,000	1,000	100	10	1
2	7	3	2	1

It is then fairly easy to add down each column from right to left, dealing with numbers of less than 10 each time.

Example: Addition

We asked what is 15,267 + 27,321?

Step one.   Write down the numbers in their columns.

10,000	1,000	100	10	1
1	5	2	6	7
2	7	3	2	1

2: NUMBERS ARE FUN

Step two.   Add down each column from right to left.

10,000	1,000	100	10	1
1	5	2	6	7
2	7	3	2	1
		5	8	8

When we get to the 1,000 column, $5 + 7 = 12$. This represents 12,000, so we write 2 in the 1,000 column and carry 1 to the 10,000 column.

10,000	1,000	100	10	1
1	5	2	6	7
2	7	3	2	1
	2	5	8	8

+1

So when we add up the 10,000 column, we have $1 + 2 = 3 + 1$ (from the addition of the 1,000 column) ie 4.

10,000	1,000	100	10	1
1	5	2	6	7
2	7	3	2	1
4	2	5	8	8

Therefore the answer to the question is:

$15,267 + 27,321 = 42,588$.

When a negative number is added to a positive number, the effect is to subtract the negative from the positive.

(a) $10 + (-6) = 10 - 6 = 4$
(b) $10 + (-12) = 10 - 12 = -2$

We will look at subtraction in more detail in the next section.

Activity 2.1

Work out the following, without using a calculator.

(a) $10 + 17$
(b) $217 + 1,420$
(c) $10,777 + 259,321$
(d) $1,572,651 + 10,321,123$

Activity 2.2

Now let's try adding more than two numbers together. Again, do not use a calculator.

Tutorial note. Don't panic, just follow the same rules as before.

(a)   10 + 100 + 1,000
(b)   2,760 + 4,320 + 5,111
(c)   4,765 + 2,277 + 3,512
(d)   1,234 + 11,234 + 22,777
(e)   1,234 + 5,678 + 9,101 + 2,468 + 3,579

4 Subtraction

Subtraction means taking one number away from another. If you have two apples and give one away, you are left with one. In maths, this is shown as $2 - 1 = 1$.

Once again, problems can occur with large numbers. However you can use the same method as for addition. Just remember to subtract the numbers in each column.

Example: Subtraction

What is $27,321 - 15,267$?

Step one: Write down the numbers in their columns.

10,000	1,000	100	10	1
2	7	3	2	1
1	5	2	6	7

Step two: Subtract the lower number from the top number in each column, working from right to left. Immediately, we find a problem as we cannot take 7 from 1 without forming a negative number. The solution is to 'borrow' 10 from the next column. We then have $11 - 7 = 4$. This time we put -1 under the '10' column to show that we have taken 10 down to the 1 column.

10,000	1,000	100	10	1
2	7	3	2	1
1	5	2	6	7
				4
			−1	+10

When we come to the tens column, we have 2 – 6 – 1. Once again we borrow 10 from the next column, so we have 12 – 6 – 1 = 5.

10,000	1,000	100	10	1
2	7	3	2	1
1	5	2	6	7
1	2	0	5	4
		-1	-1 + 10	+10

The answer is 12,054.

If you are uncertain about the answer, remember that if you add 12,054 to 15,267, it should equal 27,321:

12,054

15,267

27,321

When a negative number is subtracted from another number, the effect is to add them together.

(a)   12 – (–8) = 12 + 8 = 20
(b)   –12 – (–8) = –12 + 8 = –4

Activity 2.3

Work out the following, without using a calculator.

(a)   17 – 10
(b)   1,368 – 521
(c)   1,987,654 – 876,543
(d)   257,741, 999 – 172,511,321

Activity 2.4

Now try these, without using a calculator.

Tutorial note. When subtracting more than two numbers, take the calculation in stages. For example: 500 – 200 – 150, 500 – 200 = 300 – 150 = 150. Alternatively 500 – 200 – 150 is the same as 500 – (200 + 150) = 500 – 350 = 150. (In maths, calculations in brackets are done first.)

(a)   500 – 300 – 150
(b)   1,700 – 1,300 – 200
(c)   10,000 – 5,761 – 3,299
(d)   5,000 – 1,111 – 2,222
(e)   100,000 – 9,762 – 12,321 – 25,750

5 Multiplication

When you multiply numbers, you are effectively adding the same number together a number of times. So 3 + 3 + 3 = 9, can also be written 3 × 3 = 9. Also 100 + 100 + 100 + 100 = 400, is the same as 4 × 100 = 400.

So multiplication is a quick way of adding a lot of numbers together. For example, 10 × 325 is quicker than adding 325 to 325 ten times.

What happens when you need to multiply large numbers? What is 27,321 × 525?

We split the multiplication into stages, effectively multiplying by 500, 20 and 5, and adding the results together.

Example: Multiplication

What is 27,321 × 525?

Step one: Multiply 27,321 by 500. To do this, we multiply by 5 and then 100. In the '10' column, 5 × 2 = 10. As in addition, we carry forward the 10 to the 100 column.

10,000	1,000	100	10	1	
2	7	3	2	1	
				5	×
			0	5	
		+1			

When we come to the '100' column, we have 3 × 5 = 15 + 1 = 16. Write down 6 in the '100' column and carry forward the 10 to the '1,000' column.

100,000	10,000	1,000	100	10	1	
	2	7	3	2	1	
					5	×
1	3	6	6	0	5	
+1	+3	+1	+1			

We have: 27,321 × 5 = 136,605

and: 136,605 × 100 = 13,660,500

So: 27,321 × 500 = 13,660,500

Tutorial note. When multiplying by 10, simply add a '0' on to the end of the number, so $1,000 \times 10 = 10,000$. When multiplying by 100, add '00' to the end, so $10,000 \times 100 = 1,000,000$

Step two: Multiply 27,321 by 20. To do this we multiply by 2 and then by 10.

10,000	1,000	100	10	1	
2	7	3	2	1	
				2	×
5	4	6	4	2	
+1					

We have: $27,321 \times 2 = 54,642$

and: $54,642 \times 10 = 546,420$

So: $27,321 \times 20 = 546,420$

Step three: Multiply 27,321 by 5. We have already done this in step one: $27,321 \times 5 = 136,605$.

Step four: Add the results of steps one, two and three together.

	10,000,000	1,000,000	100,000	10,000	1,000	100	10	1
(27,321 × 500)	1	3	6	6	0	5	0	0
(27,321 ×20)			5	4	6	4	2	0
(27,321 × 5)			1	3	6	6	0	5
	1	4	3	4	3	5	2	5
		+1	+1	+1	+1			

So $27,321 \times 525 = 14,343,525$.

When two negative numbers are multiplied together, the result is positive.

(a) $(-8) \times (-4) = 32$
(b) $(-18) \times (-3) = 54$

If a positive number is multiplied by a negative number, the result is negative.

(a) $(-8) \times 4 = -32$
(b) $18 \times (-3) = -54$

Activity 2.5

Work out the following, try not to use a calculator.

(a) 12×7
(b) 525×5
(c) $1,525 \times 27$
(d) $179,321 \times 50$

Activity 2.6

Here are some more multiplications; take them step by step.

(a) $760 \times 5 \times 2$
(b) $1,275 \times 3 \times 3$
(c) $1,000 \times 5 \times 7$
(d) $5,731 \times 25 \times 4$

6 Division

You are probably not surprised to learn that division is a way of subtracting a number of times.

When we divide 144 by 12, we are simply seeing how many times we can subtract 12 from 144.

However, with large numbers, it can take a long time to keep subtracting a number.

So there is a quicker method of dividing by looking at the underlying numbers.

Example: Division

When dividing 144 by 12, you could keep subtracting 12 until you got to zero. However it is faster to use the following method.

Step one: Look at the underlying numbers, this time working from left to right.

	100	10	1
	1	4	4

Step two: Divide each number by 12. One cannot be divided by 12, so transfer the 1 from the '100' column to become 10 in the '10' column (as in subtraction). We then have $14 \div 12$. We have one twelve, leaving two over ($14 - 12 = 2$). We transfer the 2 from the '10' column to become 20 in the '1' column. So $24 \div 12 = 2$.

	100	10	1
	1	4	4
	−1	+10	+20
	-	14	24

÷ 12

		1	2

Therefore 144 ÷ 12 = 12.

A negative number divided by another negative number results in a positive number.

(a)   (−18) ÷ (−3) = +6

(b)   (−20)/(−5) = +4 (note the alternative way of denoting division by /)

A negative number divided by a positive number results in a negative number.

(a)   12/(−4) = −3

(b)   −12/4 = −3

Activity 2.7

Calculate the following, without using a calculator.

(a)   169 ÷ 13

(b)   9,639/9

(c)   175,985/5

7 Putting it all together

The title of this chapter is 'Numbers are fun'. So far we haven't been having much fun!

For the rest of this chapter, we will be playing number games based on Channel 4's 'Countdown'.

Example: Countdown

In Countdown, you are given six numbers and a total. You must add, subtract, multiply and/or divide the six numbers to arrive at the total.

You are given the numbers: 100 9 7 5 2 1 and need to arrive at 380.

There are a number of ways of getting to 380, two are shown below.

(a) 100 + 1 =   101
     9 × 7 =   63   –
                    38
     5 × 2 =   10   ×
                   380

(b) (100 − 5) =   95
     7 − 2 − 1 =   4   ×
                   380

How did we arrive at these answers? Let us look at the reasoning behind each method.

(a) 380 = 38 × 10

     5 × 2 = 10, so we need 38.

     9 × 7 = 63. This leaves us with 100 + 1 = 101.

     101 − 63 = 38

(b) 380 = 400 − 20

     400 − 20 is the same as (100 − 5) × 4

     We already have 100 and 5, can we find 4?

     7 − 2 −1 = 4.

Activity 2.8

Given the following sets of numbers, arrive at the total given.

							Total
(a)	100	9	7	5	2	1	360
(b)	75	8	3	4	1	4	614
(c)	25	8	5	1	1	2	184
(d)	50	6	3	1	2	4	624

Key learning points

- ☑ Numbers can be positive or negative.
- ☑ Numbers can be manipulated by using addition, subtraction, multiplication and division.
- ☑ Even large numbers can be added, subtracted, multiplied or divided without using a calculator.

Quick quiz

1   What is 1,562,739 multiplied by 500?

2   Given the numbers: 75   9   7   4   3   2, arrive at a total of 500.

Answers to quick quiz

1

1,000,000	100,000	10,000	1,000	100	10	1	
1	5	6	2	7	3	9	
							× 5
7	8	1	3	6	9	5	
+2	+3	+1	+3	+1	+4		

$7,813,695 \times 100 = 781,369,500$

So $1,562,739 \times 500 = 781,369,500$.

2

$$75 \times 7 = \qquad 525$$
$$9 \times 3 = \qquad 27 \quad -$$
$$\underline{\qquad 2} \quad +$$
$$\underline{500}$$

Reason

Using 75, the nearest we can get to 500 is $75 \times 7 = 525$. So we need to deduct 25.

The quickest way of doing this is:

$9 \times 3 = 27 - 2 = 25$ (as above).

Alternative way:

$$(75 - 3) = \qquad 72$$
$$\underline{\qquad 7} \quad \times$$
$$504$$
$$\underline{\qquad 4} \quad -$$
$$\underline{500}$$

This has arisen from the fact that $7 \times 3 = 21 + 4 = 25$. So instead of multiplying just the 75 by 7, we can multiply $(75 - 3)$ by 7.

chapter 3

Basic maths techniques

Contents

1 Introduction

Look at the diagram below.

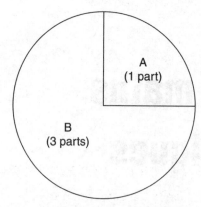

The circle consists of A plus B, ie 1 part plus 3 parts, so it is 4 parts in total.

Fractions, decimals, percentages and ratios simply show the relationship of A and B to the whole circle, or to each other.

With fractions, A is one part out of a total of four and is shown as ¼. Similarly B is ¾. The total circle is four parts out of four, ie $^4/_4$ or 1.

In decimals, A is 0.25 of the whole and B is 0.75 of the whole. From this you will realise that the whole is 1.00 in decimals.

When looking at percentages, the whole is 100%, A is 25% and B is 75%. You may have noticed that a percentage is a decimal multiplied by 100.

Finally, a ratio expresses the relationship of A to B, in mathematical notation this is A:B. In our example, A:B is 1:3. This means that A has 1 part, B has 3 parts and the whole is 4 parts (1 + 3).

Do not worry if you did not understand the above points, each will be explained in Sections 2 to 5 below. In Section 6, we will look at square roots.

2 Fractions

As we saw above, A is ¼ of the circle and B is ¾ of the circle. Notice that A and B together form the whole circle. Using fractions ¼ + ¾ = 1, so in fractions the whole is 1.

When adding fractions together, we find a common number on the bottom (called the denominator) and then add the top figures (the numerators) together.

Example: Adding fractions

(a) $\dfrac{1}{4} + \dfrac{3}{4} = \dfrac{1+3}{4} = \dfrac{4}{4} = 1$

(b) $\frac{1}{8} + \frac{5}{16}$. Here we need to find a common denominator. As $8 \times 2 = 16$, we multiply the top and bottom of $\frac{1}{8}$ by 2 = $\frac{2}{16}$. Then we can add them together.

$$\frac{1}{8} + \frac{5}{16} = \frac{2}{16} + \frac{5}{16}$$

$$= \frac{2+5}{16}$$

$$= \frac{7}{16}$$

(c) $\frac{1}{5} + \frac{1}{3}$. Again we need to find a common denominator. If we take 5×3, this equals 15. We then multiply the numerator of the first fraction by 3 and the second by 5.

$$\frac{1}{5} + \frac{1}{3} = \frac{1 \times 3}{5 \times 3} + \frac{1 \times 5}{3 \times 5}$$

$$= \frac{3}{15} + \frac{5}{15}$$

$$= \frac{3+5}{15}$$

$$= \frac{8}{15}$$

We do a similar method when subtracting fractions.

Example: Subtracting fractions

(a) $\frac{3}{4} - \frac{1}{4} = \frac{3-1}{4} = \frac{2}{4}$. Notice that 4 can be divided by 2, so the fraction $\frac{2}{4}$ is the same as $\frac{1}{2}$, ie a half. It Is usual to **simplify** fractions in this way.

(b) $\frac{5}{16} - \frac{1}{8} = \frac{5}{16} - \frac{2 \times 1}{2 \times 8}$

$$= \frac{5-2}{16}$$

$$= \frac{3}{16}$$

(c) $\frac{1}{3} - \frac{1}{5} = \frac{1 \times 5}{3 \times 5} - \frac{1 \times 3}{5 \times 3}$

$$= \frac{5}{15} - \frac{3}{15}$$

$$= \frac{5-3}{15}$$

$$= \frac{2}{15}$$

(d) $\quad \frac{3}{4} - \frac{1}{3} \quad = \quad \frac{3 \times 3}{4 \times 3} - \frac{1 \times 4}{3 \times 4}$

$$= \frac{9}{12} - \frac{4}{12}$$

$$= \frac{9-4}{12}$$

$$= \frac{5}{12}$$

Now try the following activity.

Activity 3.1

Calculate the answers to the following, using the diagram when needed.

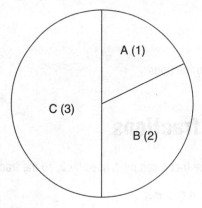

(a)   What is the fraction formed by B/C?
(b)   What is A/C?
(c)   What is the total number of parts of the whole circle?
(d)   What is A as a fraction of the whole circle?
(e)   What is B as a fraction of the whole circle?
(f)   What is C as a fraction of the whole circle?
(g)   Add together the fractions found in parts (d) and (e) above.
(h)   Add together the answers to (f) and (g) above.

BPP
PROFESSIONAL EDUCATION

Activity 3.2

Calculate the following. Do **not** use a calculator!

(a) $\frac{3}{8} - \frac{1}{6} + \frac{1}{4}$

(b) $\frac{7}{8} - \frac{1}{4} - \frac{1}{2}$

(c) $1 - \frac{5}{12} + \frac{7}{12}$

3 Decimals

Fractions like ¾ are really another way of writing 3 divided by 4.

If we actually carry out this division, we obtain a decimal. Remember in both cases the whole is 1.

Example: Obtaining decimals from fractions

Use your calculator to divide 3 by 4. You should get the answer 0.75. So ¾ is the same as 0.75.

Also ½ = 0.5 and ¼ = 0.25.

If you are not sure why this is so, see below.

1	0.1	0.01	
3	0	0	
	+30	+20	÷ 4
0	7	5	

The answer is 0.75.

Sometimes when we carry out the division, the numbers do not end. For example, $\frac{2}{3}$ is 0.66666 .... without end. This is called 0.6666 **recurring** in maths.

So what do we do with a recurring number? It is usual to round off the number after a certain number of 'significant figures' or 'decimal places'.

3.1 Significant figures and decimal places

We discard figures higher than say five significant figures. If the first discarded figure is less than five, we ignore it. If the first discarded figure is five or more, we add one onto the last figure we keep.

If we look at $\frac{2}{3}$ again, we can express it as a decimal in the following ways.

- Correct to three decimal places (ie three numbers after the decimal point)

  $\frac{2}{3} = 0.667$

- Correct to two decimal places (ie two numbers after the decimal point)

  $\frac{2}{3} = 0.67$

- Correct to three significant figures (ie the first three numbers ignoring the decimal point)

  $\frac{2}{3} = 0.67$

- Correct to four significant figures

  $\frac{2}{3} = 0.667$

Example: Significant figures

(a)   187.392 correct to 5 significant figures is 187.39. We have discarded the 2, which is less than 5 and so nothing is added to the final 9.

(b)   187.392 correct to 4 significant figures is 187.4. Discarding the 9 means 1 is added to the 3.

(c)   187.392 correct to 3 significant figures is 187. Discarding the 3 means nothing is added to the 7.

Example: Decimal places

(a)   187.392 correct to two decimal places is 187.39.
(b)   187.392 correct to one decimal place is 187.4.

Activity 3.3

Use your calculator to turn the fraction $\frac{29}{35}$ into a decimal. Round your answer in the following ways.

(a)   Correct to 5 significant figures.
(b)   Correct to 4 significant figures.

(c)   Correct to 3 significant figures.

(d)   Correct to 5 decimal places.

(e)   Correct to 4 decimal places.

(f)   Correct to 3 decimal places.

4 Percentages

Percentages are obtained from decimals and fractions by multiplying by 100%. To turn a percentage back into a fraction or decimal divide by 100%.

Consider the following.

(a) $\dfrac{4}{5} = \dfrac{4}{5} \times 100\% = \dfrac{400}{5}\% = 80\%$

(b) $0.8 = 0.8 \times 100\% = 80\%$

(c) $40\% = \dfrac{40\%}{100\%} = \dfrac{40}{100} = \dfrac{2}{5} = 0.4$

In the context of the circle in Section 1, A is 0.25 of the whole. This is 25% of the total circle.

To find a percentage of a number, divide by 100 and multiply by the percentage.

Example: Percentages (1)

Fred Bloggs' salary is £50,000 per annum. He is to get a 5% increase. How much is his new salary?

$$
\begin{aligned}
\text{Increase is 5\% of £50,000} \quad &= \quad \frac{5}{100} \times 50,000 \\[2ex]
&= \quad \frac{5 \times 50,000}{100} \\[2ex]
&= \quad \frac{250,000}{100} \\[2ex]
&= \quad 2,500
\end{aligned}
$$

So new salary is £50,000 + £2,500 = £52,500.

Example: Percentages (2)

You may have realised that Fred Bloggs' new salary is 105% of his old salary. This arises from the fact that his current salary is 100% and the increase is 5%, so his new salary is 105% of his current salary.

New salary   =   105% × £50,000

$$= \frac{105}{100} \times 50,000$$

$$= \frac{105 \times 50,000}{100}$$

= £52,500 (use your calculator to check this).

Activity 3.4

You have £10 in your wallet. After a shopping trip, you find you have spent £7.50. How much is left? Express the answer as a percentage of the original £10.

Activity 3.5

A travel agent is offering a 17% discount on the brochure price of a holiday in the Algarve. The brochure price of the holiday is £395. Calculate the discounted price.

Sometimes you may be given the new figure and need to calculate the starting point, ie the 100% figure.

Example: Percentages (3)

A shop sells a TV set for £175, after giving a cash discount of 5% on the original selling price. What was the original selling price?

The trick is to decide which figure is 100%. The discount is given on the original selling price. So the original selling price is 100%. The cash discount is 5% of the original selling price and so the £175 is 95%.

The original selling price = $\frac{175}{95} \times 100$ = £184.21. (Remember that you are dealing with money, so round to two decimal places. In this way you have whole pence!)

In order to check your answer, notice that 5% × £184.21 = £9.21 and so the TV set was sold for (£184.21 − £9.21) ie £175.

Activity 3.6

A shop sells fridges for £200, after charging a mark-up of 20% on cost. What is the original cost?

Activity 3.7

In activity 3.6, suppose you were told that the fridges sell for £200, making a gross profit margin of 5%. What is the original cost?

Tutorial note. A gross profit margin of 5% is calculated on selling price. Therefore selling price is the 100% figure.

5 Ratios

As we saw in Section 1, the ratio of A:B was 1:3.

Suppose Tom has £12 and Dick has £8. What is the ratio of Tom's cash to Dick's cash? The answer is 12:8. This can be simplified, like a fraction, to 3:2 (by dividing both sides by 4).

Example: Ratios

Tom and Dick have £24 that they wish to share in the ratio of 2:1. How much will each receive?

The total number of parts is 2 + 1 = 3

The value of one part = £24 ÷ 3 = £8

Tom's share is 2 parts = 2 × £8 = £16

Dick's share is 1 part = 1 × £8 = £8

Check: The total given to Tom and Dick is £16 + £8 = £24.

Activity 3.8

(a)   A, B, C and D want to share £600 in the ratio 6:1:2:3. How much will each receive?

(b)   A, B and C share £1,000 in the ratio: 5:3:2. How much does each receive?

(c)   Bob, Charlie and Dave have £100. They want to share it in the ratio 4:3:3. How much does each receive?

(d)   A, B, C and D have won £12,000 on the lottery. They want to share it in the ratio 2:2:1:1 based on the amounts they put into the syndicate. How much does each receive?

6 Square roots

A square of a number is the number multiplied by itself.

Therefore the square of 2 is $2 \times 2 = 4$.

A square root goes the other way to find the number originally squared. So the square root of 4 is 2.

In mathematical notation, this is shown as $\sqrt{4} = 2$.

Example: square roots

(a) $\sqrt{64} = 8$

(b) $\sqrt{121} = 11$

(c) $\sqrt{625} = 25$

The quick way to calculate a square root is to use your calculator. Input the number and then press the 'sqrt' function. This will calculate the square root for you.

Activity 3.9

Calculate the square roots of the following numbers. You may use a calculator, if necessary.

(a) $\sqrt{16}$

(b) $\sqrt{900}$

(c) $\sqrt{3,025}$

(d) $\sqrt{14,641}$

Key learning points

☑ A **decimal** is obtained from a **fraction** by carrying out the division.

☑ Decimals are usually **rounded** to a number of **significant figures** or **decimal places**.

☑ **Percentages** are obtained from decimals by multiplying by 100%.

☑ Ratios show the **proportion** of one share to another.

☑ **Square roots** can be found easily using a calculator.

Quick quiz

1   3¾ is a **fraction/decimal/percentage**.

2   1004.002955 to 9 significant figures is .....

3   Express 0.25 and ¾ as percentages.

4   What is $\sqrt{100}$?

Answers to quick quiz

1   Fraction.

2   1004.00296, discarding the final 5 adds 1 to the second 5.

3   $0.25 = 0.25 \times 100\% = 25\%$

   ¾ $= 0.75 \times 100\% = 75\%$

4   $10 (10 \times 10 = 100)$

Formulae and equations

Contents

1 Introduction

We have already been using formulae and equations during the previous two chapters of this book!

A formula is just a way of writing something in mathematical notation. It is a form of shorthand for something that can vary.

Equations are just a way of showing that two things are the same, so 1 + 2 = 3 is an equation.

2 What is a formula?

A formula is mathematical shorthand.

In the last chapter, we said that a percentage is a decimal multiplied by 100%.

We can build a formula by having p represent a percentage and d a decimal. The formula is then:

p = d × 100%

Notice that a formula is true no matter what figures are used.

Example: A formula

We have the formula:

p = d × 100%

- (a) If d = 0.10, what is p?

    p = 0.10 × 100%

       = 10%

- (b) If p = 25%, what is d?

    p   = d × 100%

    25% = d × 100%

    25% = 0.25 × 100%

    So d = 0.25

Activity 4.1

Using the formula, p = d × 100%, calculate the following.

(a)   If p = 25, what is d?
(b)   If d = 0.75, what is p?
(c)   If d = 0.50, what is p?

3 Manipulating formulae

Formulae is the plural of formula, so we have one formula but two formulae.

We can manipulate formulae to find an unknown quantity. In fact we have already done this in the example above.

Example: Manipulating a formula

In (b) above, we needed to find d.

p = d × 100%

We can divide both sides by 100% to give:

$$\frac{p}{100\%} = \frac{d \times 100\%}{100\%}$$

$$\frac{p}{100\%} = d$$

We can rewrite this as:

$$d = \frac{p}{100\%}$$

If p = 25%, what is d?

$$d = \frac{25\%}{100\%}$$

$$= 0.25$$

If p = 75%, what is d?

$$d = \frac{75\%}{100\%}$$

$$= 0.75$$

Usually, in maths, a formula is written along the lines of:

x + y = 7

You can then solve x, given various values for y and vice versa.

Activity 4.2

Solve the following:

(a)   If x + y = 7, and x = 2, what is y?

(b)   If x + y = 10, and y = –4, what is x?

(c)   If x + y = 70, what is the value of y in terms of x?

(d)   If $\dfrac{x}{y}$ = 0.75 and x = 3, what is y?

4 Simple linear equations

We have been using equations all the way through this text.

Refer back to the Countdown example in Chapter 2. We can write the answer in (a) as an equation.

$[(100 + 1) - (9 \times 7)] \times (5 \times 2) = 380$

4.1 Order of operations

In the equation above, the brackets indicate which operations we do first.

So, in the equation above, there are four sets of brackets. We must carry out the operations in the innermost brackets before those in the outermost brackets.

$$
\begin{aligned}
[(100 + 1) - (9 \times 7)] \times (5 \times 2) &= [101 - 63] \times 10 \\
&= 38 \times 10 \\
&= 380
\end{aligned}
$$

4.2 Simple linear equations

In Chapter 3, we had the example of someone having £10 and spending £7.50. You were asked how much was left.

You can write this as an equation by calling the unknown amount (the amount left) x.

Hopefully you will agree that x + 7.50 = 10.00. This is the maths way of saying the amount left (x) plus the amount spent (£7.50) equals the amount you had originally (£10).

This equation is a **simple linear equation**.

Example: Solving simple linear equations

x + 7.50	=	10.00

(deduct 7.50 from both sides)

x	=	10.00 − 7.50
	=	2.50

So the amount left was £2.50.

Example: Number puzzle

*	♦	♥	♠	15
♥	♠	♠	♥	16
♥	♦	*	♣	23
♣	*	♠	♣	23
27	11	13	26	

*	♠	♦	♥	♣
4				

This puzzle is really just a set of equations, where we are given that * = 4.

So the top row across is:

$$4 + ♦ + ♥ + ♠ = 15$$

The second row across is

$$♥ + ♠ + ♠ + ♥ = 16$$

We can rewrite this as

$$2♥ + 2♠ = 16 \qquad \text{(divide both sides by 2)}$$
$$♥ + ♠ = 8$$

Put this into the first equation:

$$4 + ♦ + 8 = 15$$
$$♦ + 12 = 15 \qquad \text{(deduct 12 from both sides)}$$
$$♦ = 3$$

In the second column down:

$$\blacklozenge + \spadesuit + \blacklozenge + * = 11$$
$$3 + \spadesuit + 3 + 4 = 11$$
$$\spadesuit + 10 = 11$$
$$\spadesuit = 1$$

Returning to the second row across:

$$2\heartsuit + 2\spadesuit = 16$$
$$2\heartsuit + (2 \times 1) = 16 \qquad \text{(deduct 2 from both sides)}$$
$$2\heartsuit = 14 \qquad \text{(divide both sides by 2)}$$
$$\heartsuit = 7$$

We just need to find out what ♣ is worth.

In the final row across:

$$2\clubsuit + * + \spadesuit = 23$$
$$2\clubsuit + 4 + 1 = 23 \qquad \text{(deduct 5 from both sides)}$$
$$2\clubsuit = 18 \qquad \text{(divide both sides by 2)}$$
$$\clubsuit = 9$$

We now have the solution to all the symbols:

*	♠	♦	♥	♣
4	1	3	7	9

Check that this is correct by looking at all the rows and columns and making sure that they come to the totals shown.

Activity 4.3

Now try this number puzzle.

*	♠	♦	*	27
♦	♥	♣	♠	16
♥	*	*	♦	24
♣	♣	♠	♥	13
18	19	21	22	

*	♠	♦	♥	♣
				2

Key learning points

☑   A formula is a way of stating a relationship between two items.

☑   Formulae can be manipulated to find the unknown item.

☑   You should now be familiar with the way of solving a number of unknowns using linear equations.

Quick quiz

1   Write a formula to express the equation in Activity 3.6.

2   $(x + y) \times 2 = 100 + x$. If $y = 30$, what is x?

3   $x + 2y = 90 - x$. If $x = 20$, what is y?

Answers to quick quiz

1   Original cost = x

$120\% \times x = 200$

2

$$(x + 30) \times 2 = 100 + x$$
$$2x + 60 = 100 + x \quad \text{(deduct 60 from each side)}$$
$$2x = 40 + x \quad \text{(deduct x from each side)}$$
$$x = 40$$

3

$$20 + 2y = 90 - 20 \quad \text{(deduct 20 from each side)}$$
$$2y = 90 - 40$$
$$2y = 50 \quad \text{(divide both sides by 2)}$$
$$y = 25$$

chapter 5

Accuracy and
approximation

Contents

1 Introduction

Sometimes it is impossible to be completely accurate.

In Chapter 3, we saw that recurring numbers are abbreviated (or **rounded**) to a number of decimal places or significant figures.

This rounding can lead to **errors**.

Sometimes there is not enough information and we have to **estimate** a number.

2 Accuracy and errors

2.1 Rounding

We have already met a form of founding in Chapter 3.

There are three methods of rounding and these will be illustrated using the figure 18,600.

(a) **Rounding up**. 18,600 is expressed as 19,000 to the nearest thousand above.

(b) **Rounding down**. 18,600 is expressed as 18,000 to the nearest thousand below.

(c) **Rounding to the nearest round amount.** 18,600 is 19,000 to the nearest thousand. This is the most commonly used method.

In rounding to the **nearest unit**, a value ending in 0.5 is usually rounded up. Thus 3.5 rounded to the nearest unit would be 4.

Rounding can be specified to the **nearest whole unit** (as above), by the **number of decimal places** (3.94712 to 2 decimal places is 3.95), or by the **number of significant figures** (as covered in Chapter 3).

Activity 5.1

(a) What is £482,365.15 to the nearest:

(i)	£1	
(ii)	£100	
(iii)	£1,000	
(iv)	£10,000	

(b)   What is 843.668 correct to:

(i)	one decimal place	
(ii)	two decimal places?	

2.2 Spurious accuracy

Spurious accuracy arises when a statistic gives the impression that it is more accurate than it really is.

Example: Spurious accuracy

Suppose we see stated in a magazine '24.68% of women over the age of 30 are smokers'. This result is probably based on a sample and so we know that it cannot be as accurate as it seems: the two decimal places have arisen simply because of the arithmetic of the calculations. It would be less misleading to state 'approximately 25% of women over the age of 30 are smokers'. This removes the spurious accuracy implied by the decimal places.

2.3 Errors

Rounding can lead to errors in calculations. So sometimes it is better to state that the answer is **approximate**.

3 Approximation

When calculations are made using rounded figures, the answers are only **approximate**.

Therefore the answer should be **rounded** to the same extent that the underlying figures were.

Example: Approximation

(a)   2/3 = 0.667 to three decimal places. This is an **approximation** of the true decimal, which is 0.666 recurring.

If we then want to calculate 2/3 × 2/3, we may use 0.667 × 0.667. Use your calculator to find the answer.

0.667 × 0.667 = 0.444889

However, the answer should be rounded to three decimal places:

0.667 × 0.667 = 0.445

This reflects the fact that the underlying calculation was approximate.

(b)   A shopkeeper says that he has approximately 500 units of a product, rounding up to the nearest ten units. If he sells 25 units during a day, how many units has he left?

You might think that the answer is:

500 – 25 = 475

However, the stock of 500 has been rounded up to the nearest ten units. Therefore the sales should also be rounded up to the nearest ten units. This gives 30 units.

Number of units left = 500 – 30

                      = 470

Activity 5.2

You have approximately £20 in your pocket, rounding to the nearest £1. How much do you have left if you spend:

(a)   £2.00
(b)   £7.75
(c)   £11.39
(d)   £4.52

Key learning points

☑ It is not always possible or desirable to be completely accurate in maths.

☑ Numbers may be **rounded** to provide workable figures.

☑ Rounding is a form of **approximation**.

☑ Approximation is acceptable in maths, but calculations involving approximate numbers or estimates should not show a higher level of accuracy than the underlying numbers.

Quick quiz

1   What is 1,039,767.539 to the nearest 10,000?

2   Two figures rounded to 3 significant figures are multiplied together. How accurate is the answer?

3   3.767 is multiplied by 0.792. What is the answer to 4 significant figures.

Answers to quick quiz

1   1,040,000.

2   The answer should be rounded to 3 significant figures to reflect the underlying rounding.

3   2.983.

chapter 6

Writing business English

Contents

1 Introduction

In obtaining your AAT qualifications, you will need to be able to write reports, memos and business letters.

It is essential that you use 'business English'.

2 Writing business English

Lecturers tell BPP that one of the commonest failings of students at this stage of their studies is poor English, so if you are a bit uncertain of your skills in this area you are probably in the majority.

To be brutally frank, if your written English is poor the people who read it will think you are unintelligent. People judge by appearances. Rightly or wrongly this is a fact of life. If you do not try to do something about it, you will hinder your career progression.

If you think you need help in this area, read on. You will not be able to take in all the hints and rules that we give in one reading. You should keep these pages with you and use them as a source of reference.

2.1 Writing bad English

There are four common faults in writing a business letter or report.

(a) **Being too colloquial**, just writing down what you would **say** if you were speaking to the person you are writing to

(b) **Writing in note form**, leaving out words that you would not leave out in normal speech, let alone in formal writing

(c) **Bad spelling**

(d) **Bad punctuation**

In the remainder of this chapter we are going to go through some basic rules and some very common mistakes that people make. Some of this may take you back to primary school days, but we have tried to make the examples a little more relevant to your studies.

2.2 Sentences

Always write in full sentences. A sentence has the following characteristics.

(a) It starts with a capital letter and ends with a full stop.

(b) It must always have a minimum of one thing/person and one action (or one noun and one verb, to use the technical terms).

Clocks tick.

I am writing.

Most of the sentences you write will have an additional thing/person, with one of the things performing the action on the other one.

I am writing a book.

I am writing to you.

(c) Things or persons can be collections of words as well as single words. Though it might look more complicated the following sentence is in the standard form *person* does *thing.*

The senior manager of ABC Ltd has written a report on the future of the industry.

(d) There are two ways of looking at anything that happens.

(i) Things *perform* actions.
(ii) Actions *are performed by* things.

Method (i) is generally preferable in business writing.

(e) Sentences can, and usually will, be longer than the examples given so far. They can be joined up by words like *and* or *but* or *although,* or you can give extra information about something in the main part of your sentence using words like *who, which* or *that.*

As a general rule, in business communications, the simpler your sentences are the better. This means that you should keep them fairly short.

Try not to write sentences that are all the same length, however, because this is very monotonous to read.

2.3 Paragraphs

If you just write sentence after sentence with no breaks, your writing will be very tiring to read and difficult to follow. For this reason groups of sentences are split into paragraphs and there is a space between each paragraph.

A paragraph should have only one main idea. This may mean that it only has one sentence, or there may be additional sentences exploring the main idea, or leading up to the main idea. This paragraph that you are reading now has one main sentence (the first) and two additional sentences exploring the main idea.

In practice it is often difficult to decide where one main idea finishes and the next one starts. The rule again is to keep things short and simple but not to the extent that your writing gets monotonous.

In day to day business communications, which tend to be fairly short anyway, it will quite often be appropriate to have a new paragraph for each sentence. Most newspapers tend to be written in this style, too. In a 3,000 - 4,000 word report, however, this is liable to get very monotonous.

2.4 Brevity

Brevity is said to be the soul of wit. It is certainly essential in business writing. You must make your meaning clear, but you should use as few words as possible to do so. Superfluous words obscure the meaning and waste the reader's time.

Consider these sentences from a management text book and compare them with the edited versions.

Original sentences

- *A high staff turnover may be indicative of a wider problem such as poor morale.*
- *Identify the development areas that need to be addressed.*
- *Check to ensure that the activity has been carried out and successfully completed.*
- *The job description details the characteristics that a successful candidate would need to demonstrate.*

Edited sentences

- *A high staff turnover may indicate a wider problem such as poor morale.*
- *Identify the development areas to be addressed.*
- *Check that the activity has been carried out.*
- *The job description details the characteristics of a successful candidate.*

Overall, the word count has been reduced from 51 to 38: a 25% reduction.

It is actually quite difficult to write briefly and clearly. The secret is to **read what you have written** and ask yourself if it could be improved.

3 Common mistakes

3.1 A, an, the

These little words are the simplest in the language. They are so simple that you often leave them out in informal writing and in notes.

Do **not** leave them out in formal writing.

3.2 Etc, etc

Avoid *ie* (in other words) and *eg* (for example), and never use *etc* (and so on).

If you are tempted to use these abbreviations take note of the following points.

(a) To people who know better you will look very silly if you use *ie* when you mean *eg* or *eg* when you mean *ie*. This is a very common mistake.

    (i) You use *ie* when you are *clarifying* what you have just said.

        ... any of the standard colours available, ie green, red or blue.

        This fell off the back of a lorry, ie it is stolen.

    (ii) You use *eg* if you are only giving selected *examples* (or a single example) of what you have just said rather than a complete list.

        ... any colour you like, eg sea-green, pillar-box red, tartan, pink ... .

> *... retailers, eg Sainsbury's ...*

To avoid mistakes do as we suggest initially: don't use these abbreviations at all!

(b)   Either punctuate properly or don't punctuate at all. Do one or the other consistently.

| *i.e.* | *e.g.* | *etc.* | OR | *ie* | *eg* | *etc* |

| BUT NOT | *ie.* | *eg.* | *e.t.c.* |

(c)   When you write **etc** at the end of a list, you are saying that both you and the reader know perfectly well all the other items which are needed to make the list absolutely complete. The only occasion when this is likely to be true is if you have given the complete list earlier. If you are tempted to use *etc* ask yourself if you can think of any more items. If you can, write them down instead of *etc*. If you cannot, do not write *etc* hoping that readers will think you could if you wanted to. They will almost certainly assume the opposite.

(d)   Do not forget that items in a simple list are separated by commas except for the last two which are joined by 'and'. If the items in a list consist of more than a couple of words, or if one of them includes the word 'and', use **semicolons** instead of commas. For example:

> *A competent payroll clerk should be able to deal with piecework pay; deduction of tax and national insurance; joiners and leavers; and preparation of P60s.*

3.3 Get things right and do them properly

Often you will want to say something descriptive about the things or the actions in your sentences. You do this by using one or other of two types of *description word*, depending on whether you are describing a thing or an action. One of the most common mistakes that people make is to use the wrong sort of description word.

The basic rule is that if you are describing an *action* the word you use ends with *-ly*.

Example	Explanation
These figures are incorrect.	'incorrect' describes the figures
These figures have been added up incorrectly.	'incorrectly' describes the adding up
That is bad English.	'bad' describes the English
That is badly written.	'badly' describes the writing
Get things right	'right' describes the things
Do them properly	'properly' describes how they are done

Description words that describe *actions* usually say *how* the action is done or *where* it is done or *when* it is done.

3.4 Most common or commonest?

Do you say that something is *more common* than something else or do you say it is *commoner*? The basic rules for deciding whether to add *-er* and *-est* to a word or use *more* and *most* are as follows.

(a)   If the word has only one syllable add *-er* and *-est*: *harder, longer, biggest, highest* and so on.

(b)   If the word has two syllables and ends in *-y, -er, -le* or *-ow*, add *-er* and *-est*: *likeliest, happiest, lazier, idlest, cleverest, narrower* and so on. Also add *-er* and *-est* if using the *un-* form of these words: *unlikeliest, unhappier* and so on.

(c)   Otherwise use *more* and *most*: *more difficult, more probable, most intelligent, most infuriating* and so on.

With some words you can either add *-er* and *-est* or use *more* and *most* (*common* is such a word), but if you apply the rules above you should never make a mistake.

3.5 Who's who?

Sometimes you can find yourself using words like *he, she, it* and *them* (pronouns, if you want the technical term) so much in a passage of writing that it is not clear what they refer to.

For example, consider this:

Tom, Dick and Harry were talking about their work and Tom said to Dick that he thought he was great.

Does Tom think Dick is great? Or that he is great himself? Or is he saying that Dick thinks highly of himself or, perhaps, of Harry? Or is it that Tom thinks Harry appreciates Dick? There are even more possibilities than these.

You need to read your writing carefully to check whether it contains this sort of ambiguity. To get round the problem you usually have to identify one or more of the people or things involved, using a name or description instead of, or as well as, the word he, she or it.

Jo thought <u>his supervisor</u> was great. He also thought <u>he, Jo,</u> was great.

3.6 I and me

While we are on the subject of words like *he, she* and *it* we may as well remind you about *I* and *me*. Quite simply, use the form *me* if somebody else is doing the action to you.

The company gave Lucy and me a big pay rise.

The company is doing the giving.

If you are doing the action use the form *I*.

I got a big pay rise and so did Lucy.   OR   *Lucy and I got a big pay rise.*

Here it is you who is doing the getting. The question 'Who is doing the action?' is very often the key to a good sentence, as the next few paragraphs illustrate.

3.7 Who's doing what?

Which of the following sentences is correct?

1   *The best guide are accounting standards.*

2   *The problem here is the words are and is.*

BPP
PROFESSIONAL EDUCATION

The words are and is are the problem. Do you make your action words (or verbs) singular or plural when the first thing is singular and the second thing is plural?

The answer is that it depends which comes first. Sentence 2 is the correct one. If you look carefully at sentence 2 and then go on to the sentence below it beginning 'The words ...' you will see that they say the same thing, except that the order of the words has been changed round. The use of the singular is or the plural are depends on whether what comes first is singular or plural.

If there are two things doing the action and one is singular and the other is plural what happens to the action word? For example is the following sentence correct?

References and an application form has been sent to Mr Slater.

If you think about it, Mr Slater will receive both the references and the form. In other words there are two things performing the action of being sent so the action word must be plural: in the sentence above has should say *have been sent*.

Be careful not to be distracted by words that just happen to come between the thing doing the action and the action word itself.

The source of the mistakes were not known.

It is tempting in a sentence like this to make the action word fit in with the word nearest to it (mistakes), but give it a moment's thought and you will realise that it is not the mistakes (plural) that are unknown but their source (singular): *were* should therefore be *was*.

If a word like *who* or *which* gets in the way be careful. Is this sentence correct?

An accountant is one of those professionals who helps to run businesses and gets well-paid for it.

In fact the words helps and gets are both wrong. It is professionals who help and professionals who get well-paid. The accountant is just one of these people.

3.8 Which hunting

Which is one of the most overused words in bad writing. Here is a simple explanation.

(a) *The invoice <u>that</u> we sent you last week contained an error.*

BUT

I posted that transaction to the sales ledger, <u>which</u> was a mistake.

Technically, *that* is used when it begins a series of words that *define* what has gone before. In the first example above the words beginning with *that* give information that distinguishes the invoice containing the error from any other invoice. In contrast *which* is used when the sentence changes direction slightly in order to complete the thought it expresses.

This change is indicated by the comma that precedes *which*.

(b) If it sounds better to join up the bits of your sentence with a simple *and* or *but* or to write two separate short sentences you should probably do so. Both of the following are correct but the second is better.

You will be sent two invoices, <u>which</u> you may pay together if you wish.

You will be sent two invoices <u>but</u> you may pay both together if you wish.

Don't worry unduly about this: simply be aware that if which is badly used it can get you into all sorts of difficulties that could easily have been avoided.

3.9 Who and whom

Strictly, when *who* is the person having an action done to them the form to use is *whom*.

The customers to whom these invoices were sent have all complained.

If you are confident about using whom then do so by all means. In speech, though, you would probably have said The customers who these invoices were sent to have all complained. Likewise in modern business writing it is probably not worth worrying unduly about whom. So long as you are keeping things short and simple it will not offend many people if you break the rule.

A related problem is whether it is allowable to end a sentence with what is technically known as a *preposition*: a 'position' word like *to* or *with* or *from*. In general try to avoid doing so, but do not worry unduly about it. There is a famous example of how badly wrong you can go if you try too hard to avoid it.

That is something up with which I will not put.

This is taking the rules to extremes. It makes it harder, not easier, for people to follow your writing. In fact it is something that readers should not be expected to put up with!

3.10 Do you or are you doing?

What is the difference between *I write* and *I am writing*? This is a frequent problem for people who learned another language before they learned English, because other languages do not make a distinction.

Sometimes it doesn't matter which form you use, but sometimes it does. If you are not sure which is correct instinctively, follow these simple rules and you will never make a mistake.

    (a)   If you are actually doing the action at the time when you are saying that you are doing it, use the *I am doing...* form.

    (b)   If you do the thing as a normal ongoing part of your life but you are not actually doing it at the time when you are talking or writing use the *I do* form.

        Here is an example.

        We <u>are investigating</u> your complaint and will write to you again when we have completed our enquiries.

        We <u>investigate</u> all complaints fully and offer compensation if we prove to be at fault.

Similar rules can be applied to *I was doing* and *I did* (the first takes you back to a time when the action was actually being done; the second makes you think that though someone did it in the past it is now finished) but in this case either form is usually acceptable.

3.11 To boldly go

One of the forms of an action word is the *to* form: *to do, to calculate, to be, to decide* and so on. The *to* should be regarded as something that cannot be separated from the main action word. You do not write *to quickly calculate*. The correct form is *to calculate quickly*. This rule is based on Latin grammar, so it is really quite obsolete and shouldn't be followed slavishly in English. Most people break this rule in everyday speech and many people break it in their writing. However many others – quite possibly including some of the people that you write to – get annoyed by it. The safest option, therefore, is not to break the rule.

It is sometimes better to avoid the problem by changing the *to* form to something else.

We used to regularly send out statements, but this tends to get neglected now.

You could correct this by changing it to: *We used to send out statements regularly ...* . This is fine, but another possibility, if you wanted to leave *regularly* where it is, would be the following.

At one time we regularly sent out statements ...

3.12 Going too boldly

Never write *to* when what you mean is *too*. If your work is typed up always check that the typist has not typed *to* when you want *too*. This point is made again in the section on spelling but it is such a common mistake that it is worth giving you advance warning.

3.13 Try to get it right

You might often say to someone *I'm going to try and do that*. This is wrong because *and* is a word used to join up two separate things, whereas the *trying* and the *doing* are not two separate things. What you mean is that you are going to *try to do* whatever it is.

RIGHT	*Go and see what the matter is*	Going *and* seeing are two different things
WRONG	*Try and improve your writing skills*	Trying *to* improve is all one action

3.14 Should have

It is very easy to write *I should of done that by half past three*. You write this because in terms of pronunciation it is very close to what you say. It is never, ever correct, though, whatever your ears tell you.

What you really mean is *I should have done that ...* . The same problem arises and the same mistake is often made with *could*.

WRONG	*I could of finished that if the phone had not rung.*
RIGHT	*I could have finished that if the phone had not rung.*

3.15 Off with of

Since we are on the subject of *of* it is worth saying that just because you go *down to* the shops or *out of* the country or *up to* someone in the street, you do not get *off of* a bus. The word *off* is always quite happy on its own: you *get off a bus*. It is never correct to write *off of*, so you do not *collect the papers off of Mr Jones*, you collect them *from* Mr Jones.

3.16 Should and would

Since we are also on the subject of *should* it is worth mentioning the conventional way to ask someone to do something in business writing.

I should be grateful if you would settle this account.

Note that should is used with I and would is used with you. This is because should has the sense of ought to and would has the sense of be willing: using should and would like this is just a way of being polite. However so many people write I would be grateful nowadays that this, too, has become perfectly acceptable.

3.17 Their, there and they're

A common mistake is to use *their* when you mean *there* or using *they're* when you mean *their* or any other permutation of this error. Always check your writing to make sure that you have got these words right. This is not just a spelling problem: the three words have completely different meanings.

For a start you can make life a little easier for yourself by not using the form *they're* (they are) in formal writing: then there is one fewer to get wrong.

You probably know which spelling is right in different contexts, but it is very easy to write the wrong one as a slip of the pen. Here are some checks you can carry out to avoid this.

Their   in front of word is a neater way of writing *belonging to them* after it. If your sentence becomes nonsense when you cross out the word *their* and put in the words *belonging to them* you have the wrong word.

         Which of the following sentences is wrong?

         Students should always check there writing for common mistakes.

         Their is a good reason for checking words like this.

         The first sentence could be reworded: 'Students should always check the writing **belonging to them** for common mistakes'. The word there should therefore be spelled their. In the second sentence you cannot fit in the words belonging to them at all: it doesn't make sense. The word their should therefore be spelled there. Both of the sentences are wrong.

There   is the word to use if the next word is *is* or *are*. *There* can often be thought of as a similar word to *here*: in fact of course, it is just *here* with a *t* in front, and it indicates that something exists.

         There are the papers you asked for.   *Here are the papers ...*

         There are six students who always get this wrong and   *Six students exist who ...*
         they will have to pay me £5 every time they do it in
         future!

You probably think that we have made a bit of a meal of this simple point. If so, we challenge you never to make mistakes with these words again!

4 Punctuation

4.1 Capitals

Use a capital letter only in the following situations.

(a)   At the beginning of a sentence

(b)   For names of people and institutions: Peter, Jo, Nicole, Barclays Bank plc, Berisford Limited, the Foreign Office

(c)   For titles: Inspector Morse, Sir Humphrey Appleby, Mr Gomez

(d)   For places and nationalities: Manchester, Japan, Italian

(e)   Where convention demands it: I, God. (Not using capitals for *plc* is also a convention)

Do not use capital letters otherwise. For example the following (taken from a piece of writing produced by an AAT student) is wrong.

At the end of the day Invoices and Statements are run off on the Printer.

The only capital letter that is correct here is the one at the beginning of the sentence: invoices, statements and printer are general words, not names of things that are special to this particular accounting department. Capitals where they are not needed distract and irritate your readers.

4.2 Consistency

There are, however, some circumstances in which it is neither right nor wrong to use capital letters. For example you might be inclined to use capital letters for someone's job title (*Mr Akashi, the Sales Director*) or for the name of a department (*the Purchase Ledger Department*). Whatever decision you make about capitals in these cases you must be consistent within a single document: either *always* use capitals whenever you refer to them or *never* use capitals, but do not do one thing in one paragraph and another in the next.

4.3 Quotation marks

The main thing to remember about quotation marks is that you should hardly ever use them in business writing.

(a)   It is a very common and very irritating mistake to use them when you are not sure that you have chosen the right word, or when you think you are using a word in a colloquial way. It is also common, but wrong, to use them when you are referring to something that you think is unusual in context, or when you are trying to emphasise something. Avoid these errors in the following ways.

    (i)   Choose another word that is more appropriate.

(ii) Do not use highly colloquial expressions in formal written English. Ask yourself if you would use the expression if you were talking to a senior person in your organisation and wanted to make a good impression. (Would you say to your company's managing director 'Yo, MD! What's happening?' If not, do not use the expression.)

(iii) If your reader will understand the word you are using, even though it seems a bit wacky, there is no need to use quotation marks. (Find the example in the preceding sentence.)

If you are unsure, just consider whether quotation marks will *help* your reader. Putting them round the word 'wacky' does not help anybody to understand what it means. Quotation marks do not turn informal words into formal words.

(iv) Quotation marks are *never* used for emphasis. Use *italics* for emphasis if typing and <u>underline</u> the word if writing by hand.

(b) The only circumstances in which quotation marks *must* be used are these.

(i) Use them when you are quoting the words that someone actually said.

'I'm fed up with students who put quotation marks all over the place', said the tutor.

One commentator was bullish about the prospects for accounting technicians: 'This new emphasis on communication skills could mean that AAT members become one of the highest paid groups in society.'

It will be fairly rare for you to quote direct speech in business communications.

(ii) Use them when you are discussing a word or phrase *as a word or phrase*, probably prior to explaining its meaning. Really this is just a variation on the use of quotation marks for quotations.

This technique is known as 'double entry', and it involves ...

The term 'double entry' means ...

(c) In BPP books we always use single quotation marks unless there is another set within the first set. If this happens the second set are double quotation marks.

The lecturer said 'This technique is known as "double entry", and it involves ...'

In other books, and as a general rule in newspapers, you might see the opposite approach, with double being the more frequent. Either approach is acceptable as long as you consistently follow one or the other throughout a piece of writing.

4.4 Apostrophes

In modern English apostrophes are used for two different purposes.

(a) To show that something belongs to somebody or something: *employees' pay records* (meaning the *pay records of employees*).

(b) To show that a letter has been missed out in a word such as *haven't* (short for *have not*) or *they're* (short for *they are*).

4.4.1 's or s'

If the word is plural the apostrophe comes after the *s*. If the word is singular the apostrophe comes before the *s*. This is simple enough but people very often get it wrong. This is probably because they do not check. The rule, if you do not want people to think you are thick, is: *always check that your apostrophes are in the right place!*

4.4.2 Do'nt and Don't

It is best not to use forms like *don't* and *isn't* and *aren't* in formal writing. If you use them in informal communications, get the apostrophe in the right place. It goes in the place where the letter has been omitted. For example *don't* is short for *do not*: the apostrophe takes the place of the missing letter *o*.

4.4.3 Its and it's

These two words do not mean the same thing. You will always pick the right one, though if you simply remember that an apostrophe between two letters means that something has been left out between those two letters. Test by inserting the word *is* and seeing if your sentence still makes sense.

It's time you got to grips with double entry	MEANS	*It is time ...*
It's a sunny day today	MEANS	*It is a sunny day ..*
Tell me the account code and its balance	DOES NOT MEAN	*... and it is balance.*

As we have already said, an even easier way to get this right is to avoid using the form *it's* completely. Say *it is* instead.

4.4.4 Whose and who's

Apply the same rule as you apply for *its* and *it's*. If you can insert the word *is* and your sentence still makes sense the form to use is *who's*. Better, use *who is*.

4.4.5 Shop windows

People who write things in huge white letters on shop windows appear to have learned this skill at a special school that required them to make at least one mistake per window. How often have you seen something like this?

HUNDRED'S
OF
BARGAIN'S!!

Both of the apostrophes here are wrong. *Hundreds* and *bargains* are just the plural of *hundred* and *bargain*.

It is probably the word *of* that causes the confusion. If you are guilty of this error try to remember the following examples.

Dozens of students

Dozens of students' pay packets

Whenever *'s* or *s'* is used there *must* be something else in the sentence that belongs to the word with the apostrophe. In the first sentence the students are penniless so they have no apostrophe. In the second sentence the pay packets belong to them so they celebrate by adding an apostrophe.

4.5 Commas

Some people use commas to mark places in their sentences where they would pause for breath. This is totally wrong. The people who read your report will breathe as and when they need to: otherwise you would be able to suffocate people by writing extra long sentences.

(You may find that people in authority (your boss, your tutor) believe that punctuation marks are breathing marks, probably because that is what they were taught at school. Tell them to buy a little Penguin book by E V Carey called *Mind the Stop* if they do not believe BPP.)

Commas are used to make the logic of your sentence clearer. Since you will be writing relatively short simple sentences in all your business communications you should not need to use them very much at all.

Here are some simple rules for using commas. These cover the most common uses.

(a)   Use commas in lists of items.

   ... red, white, blue and green.

   ... main ledger, sales ledger and purchase ledger.

   The usual convention is not to put a comma before and and the last item, the argument being that the other commas are used in place of and. Sometimes this rule may need to be broken to make things clear, though:

   ... accounting firms such as Deloitte Touche, Baker Tilly, and Ernst and Young.

   Without the comma a reader who is not familiar with these names might think that there was a firm called Baker Tilly and Ernst and Young.

(b)   Use commas when there are bits of your sentence that could be missed out without making the sentence incomplete.

   Debits, <u>which go on the left</u>, are assets of the business.

   He said that debits go on the right, <u>which is incorrect</u>.

   Mrs Chomsky, <u>one of our leading customers</u>, has cancelled her order.

   Here you could miss out the words that are underlined and still have complete sentences.

   There are sometimes odd individual words which you could leave out without damaging the sense of your sentence, but putting commas round them is overdoing it.

   The payroll records, which were usually kept in the Personnel Department, had completely vanished.

   Here you could miss out the words usually and completely but to put commas round them would distract your reader unnecessarily. The logic of the sentence is clear without them.

(c)   Use commas between bits of your sentence that could stand alone as independent sentences but which happen to be joined together with a connecting word. This is usually only necessary with fairly long sentences.

It was suggested that the discrepancy had occurred because entries in the accounting records for the second half of the year had been posted to the wrong accounts, but this proved not to be the source of the error once a more thorough investigation had been carried out.

The general rule, with the exceptions above, is to write simple sentences and use commas as little as possible.

4.6 Exclamation marks

Do not use exclamation marks in formal business writing. In informal writing there is no reason to use more than one.

4.7 Colons: introductions

The colon is two full stops, one on top of the other. You might want to use this occasionally to introduce things.

There are two types of accounting entry: debits and credits.

You may sometimes see a colon with a dash after it (:-). This is old-fashioned. You may find that older people use it. The dash is not necessary, so leave it out.

It is very easy to type a semi-colon (;) when you mean to type a colon (:) because the two are on the same key on a typewriter. Be aware of this and check carefully that writing that has been typed up has the punctuation mark you intended.

4.8 Separations and semi-colons

A semi-colon is a comma with a full stop on top of it. You might want to use these in lists where each item in the list is more than a few words, especially if there are also commas within items in the list.

Attending the meeting were: the managing director, who did not vote; Mr Smith, representing his wife; various small shareholders, most of whom wanted to raise specific issues; and a large man, who was sheltering from the rain.

It is unlikely that you would want to write like this in a business context. It is usually clearer and simpler to have separate lines for each thing in the list.

The meeting was attended by the following people.

- *The managing director, who did not vote*
- *Mr Smith, representing his wife*
- *Various small shareholders, most of whom wanted to raise specific issues*
- *A large man, who was sheltering from the rain*

4.9 Dashes

The dash is a multi-purpose punctuation mark and because of this it can make your writing sloppy – you can easily end up dashing about all over the place – not having a clear idea of where your sentence is going – not knowing quite where to finish – and leaving your reader in doubt as to what the point of your sentence was in the first place – if there was a point.

Dashes are fine if you know how to use them correctly. On the other hand anything you can do with a dash you can do equally well with other punctuation marks. It is probably best to avoid the problems and dangers by not using them at all.

4.10 Brackets

Brackets are used to include bits of extra information within the main sentence. The rules to remember are as follows.

(a) Think of brackets as a form of double entry. For every opening bracket there must be an equal and opposite closing bracket. When you are checking your writing, the first thing you should do when you see an opening bracket is look for the closing one.

(b) If there are too many brackets you will confuse your reader. Try to have no more than one set of brackets per sentence.

(c) It should be possible to cross out the part of your sentence that is bracketed without upsetting the sense of the main part of the sentence.

Which of the following sentences is correctly punctuated?

This is the main (not the bracketed part) of the sentence.

This is the main (not the bracketed) part of the sentence.

If you cross out the bracketed part of the first sentence you are left with *This is the main of the sentence.* This does not make sense. The second version is the correct one. You should always check that you would be left with a full sentence if you cross out the part you have put in brackets.

4.11 Full stops, commas and brackets

The rules are simple.

(a) If the bracketed part of a sentence is right at the end of the sentence the full stop comes *after* the closing bracket (like this). The full stop is normally part of the main sentence, not the bracketed part (see (d)).

(b) Never put a comma, a colon or a semi-colon before an opening or closing bracket. Both of the commas in the following example are wrong and should be deleted.

... the sales ledger, (part of the accounting system,)

(c) Commas can come after a closing bracket. As usual, try crossing out the bracketed part: if the comma that follows it would be necessary in the main sentence it is correct.

Dogs (which have four legs), ducks (which have two), and spiders (which have eight) were all on the menu that evening.

(d)   If you put brackets round an entire sentence the sentence should begin with a capital letter and end with a full stop, just like any other sentence.

(The whole of this sentence is in brackets.)

It is unusual to put brackets round a whole sentence.

5 Spelling problems

A lot of bad spellers could very easily be good spellers. These are people who know there are rules about, say, dropping the *e* at the end of a word when *-ing* is added to it (*care/caring*), or doubling the *l* when a word ending in *-ful* has *-ly* added to it (*careful/carefully*). Troubles start when people forget that there are exceptions to the rules, or they get confused about when to apply the rules, or they apply them too enthusiastically.

Unfortunately there is no easy way to improve your spelling. The most pleasurable way is to read a great deal: subconscious learning is probably the main way that you have learned to spell over the years. The problem is that this process works relatively slowly.

The most difficult way to improve your spelling is to learn what is called the **etymology** of English words: that is, how they are derived from old English, old Norse, French, Latin, German and so on. If you were to do this you would realise that there are good historical reasons for words having the spellings they have today, but again it would take you years to develop the expertise.

The compromise method is to learn and remember some basic rules and to learn any individual words that you have difficulty with off by heart. You might find it more acceptable to think of this as solving problems rather than learning rules.

On the following pages we set out some basic spelling rules.

Do not try to learn the table in one sitting.

Try to use it actively. Photocopy it and carry it around with you. Perhaps try to conquer one spelling problem a day and try to find examples of the rule or hint in anything you read that day. The next day, besides conquering a new problem, go over some of the other rules that you have already learned to fix them in your long-term memory. If you follow this timetable diligently you should find that your spelling improves dramatically and permanently.

5.1 Computer spell checking

Any decent word processing package includes a built-in dictionary. If you type something on a word processor you can then click on a button and the program will work through your document pausing at any word that does not appear in its dictionary and offering you the opportunity to correct your spelling or choose an alternative word.

If you have such a tool available you would be foolish not to use it. Make it your habit always to use the spell checking facility just before you close a document.

Remember, on the other hand, that there are certain mistakes that the spell check does not pick up. For example, if you type *form* but meant to type *from* the computer will not recognise your mistake. All it is doing is seeing if the words you have typed are spelled like that in the dictionary. Other examples are typing *i* when you mean *it* (the computer thinks you mean *I*) or typing *n* when you mean *in* or *on* (because individual letters of the alphabet are valid entries in the dictionary).

You cannot rely on the computer to do all your spelling for you or to correct badly written sentences. In other words, spell checking should not be regarded as a substitute for checking through a piece of word processing material on paper with the naked eye.

5.2 Basic good spelling

Problem	Rule or hint	Examples	Exceptions
Short words	Double the last letter when adding an ending. There are many exceptions, though: these just have to be learned.	bat/batted, drop/dropping, occur/occurring, omit/omitted	debit/debited, credit/credited bus/buses great/greater
-able	Try to pronounce words with this ending as they are spelled whenever you see them.		
-al	Words ending with single -l have ll when -ly is added.	real becomes really, national becomes nationally	
-ance, -ant	Try to pronounce words with these endings as they are spelled whenever you see them.		
-c	Add k if using -ing or -ed with a word that ends with c.	panic, panicking	
-cede	This is the normal spelling for words that end in this sound. There are only four exceptions: these are given opposite and you should learn them by heart.	concede, precede, recede	exceed proceed succeed supersede
-ch	Words ending in -ch have a plural ending in -es.	church, churches	
check	This word means to examine the accuracy of something.	Always check that you have not written cheque when you mean check!	
cheque	This word means a written order to the bank to pay a stated sum.	Always check that you have not written check when you mean cheque!	

Problem	Rule or hint	Examples	Exceptions
dis-	Just add dis and leave the rest of the word unchanged. Only use ss if the word itself begins with s.	disappear, displease, dissimilar	
-ei-	This is the correct spelling after a c (but see -ie-).	receipt	species
-ence, -ent	Try to pronounce words with these endings as they are spelled whenever you see them.		
fore-	This means 'before'. Do not confuse it with for- at the beginning of a word, which has other meanings.	forecast, forewarn forget, forbid forego means 'go before' forgo means 'go without'	
-fs	Words ending in -f or -fe generally have an -s added in the plural. Exceptions change the -f to -ves (they are spelled as they are pronounced).	beliefs, chiefs, proofs, safes	halves, knives, leaves, lives, loaves, selves, wives
-ful	Words ending with single -l have ll when -ly is added.	careful becomes carefully	
-ible	Try to pronounce words with this ending as they are spelled whenever you see them.		
-ie-	The most famous spelling rule is: I before E except after C. (C + EI is the same rule for accountants).	yuppies, receive, receipt, piece	foreign, either, counterfeit, forfeit, seize, weir, weird, neighbour, species
-ie	-ie changes to -y when -ing is added. It drops the e when -ed is added.	lie, lying, lied	
-ise or -ize	There is no rule. If in doubt use -ise.	advertise, advise	American spelling and some English writers use both. For example organize is common in UK newspapers.
-ll	Change a double -ll to single -l when the word forms part of a longer word. Contrast this with the rules for -al and -ful.	full, well, till become handful, welcome, until	illness, tallness, farewell

Problem	Rule or hint	Examples	Exceptions
mis-	Just add mis. Leave the rest of the word unchanged. Only use ss if the word itself begins with s.	misunderstand, mistake, misspell	
-ness	Use -nn- if the word to which -ness is added already ends in n.	keen, keenness, green, greenness	
-oe	Always keep the e unless the added ending begins with e.	hoe, hoes, hoeing, hoed	
-oes	Most words that end in -o becomes -oes in the plural. There are several common exceptions to learn, though.	echoes, vetoes, tomatoes, potatoes	zeros, provisos, photos, radios, pianos
-our	Drop the -u- when an ending is added.	humour, humorous, honour, honorary	honourable
-s, -sh	Words ending in -s or -sh have a plural ending in -es.	boss, bosses, dress, dresses. dish, dishes	
-ss	Keep ss if adding an ending.	assess, assessment, discuss, discussion	
too	This word means either 'also' or 'more than is desirable'. Check that you have not written to when you mean too.	This is too difficult. I want to win the lottery, too.	
-ves	See -fs.		
-x	Words ending in -x have a plural ending in -es.	box, boxes	
-y	Change -y to -i if the next letter is not a vowel (a,e,i,o,u).	beauty, beautiful, easy, easily	
-y	Words ending in -y change to -ies in the plural.	company, companies, diary, diaries, party, parties	Words ending in -ay, -ey, -oy, -uy: days, keys, toys, buys
-z	Words ending in -z have a plural ending in -es.	fizz, fizzes	

Key learning points

☑ Common mistakes should be completely eradicated from your writing.

- – Do not leave out little words.
- – Do not use ie, eg and etc.
- – If you are describing an action word use the -ly form (correctly).
- – Learn the rules for -er and -est.
- – Avoid ambiguity.
- – Think about who is doing what.
- – Do not separate to from the main action word.
- – Check to and too, try to, should have, and their and there: make sure you have the right form.

☑ Use punctuation only when necessary.

- – Use capitals only at the beginning of sentences and for names of people, places and institutions.
- – Use inverted commas rarely if at all.
- – Get apostrophes in the right place. Avoid abbreviations.
- – Use commas only in lists or if essential to make the logic clear.
- – Do not use exclamation marks or dashes.
- – Get brackets in the right place.

☑ Unfortunately the only practical way to improve your spelling is to learn words off by heart. It is worth making the effort if you care at all about the impression you make on other people.

chapter 7

Computer functions

Contents

1 Introduction

Whenever a transaction takes place, it must be recorded. Records must be kept in an orderly and logical manner. In particular, the records must distinguish between the different types of transaction such as sales, capital purchases, disposals and expenses.

2 Codes

2.1 The purpose of codes

In commercial organisations, codes are often used because they can **identify** items more concisely and precisely than written descriptions. They also help to **classify** the items into groups for recording.

With the widespread use of computer accounting systems, the coding of accounts has become an integral part of the analysis of accounting data. Coding systems are designed to help with the classification of data.

2.2 Classifications and codes

Classification is 'the arrangement of items in logical groups, having regard to their nature or purpose'. A **code** is defined as 'a system of symbols designed to be applied to a classified set of items, to give a brief accurate reference, facilitating entry, collation and analysis.'

Example

Suppose that an organisation spends £500 sending one of its trainee accountants on a training course. The transaction can be classified in two ways.

(a) The **nature** of the transaction is that it is an administrative expense, so it could be coded in a way that linked it to Accounts department overheads.

(b) The **purpose** of the transaction is to provide training. Therefore it could be coded as a training expense.

2.3 The analysis of financial accounting data

A system of financial accounts centres around the personal accounts in the sales ledger and the purchase ledger, and the impersonal accounts (including the cash book) in the main ledger.

The **sales ledger** consists of the various individual accounts for each credit sale customer.

Each customer has his own account, and an account is identified by a unique customer account number (a code number) as well as by name and address.

The account can be displayed on a computer screen by keying in the account code number or selecting the appropriate record. New credit customers are given their own account, and so adding new accounts to the sales ledger is a regular accounting practice.

The **purchase ledger** is organised in a similar way to the sales ledger.

The **main ledger** is slightly more complex. It contains details of assets, liabilities and capital, income and expenditure, and hence profit and loss. It consists of a large number of different accounts, each account having its own purpose, name and identity code.

2.3.1 Grouping

Fixed assets	*Code*
Land and buildings at cost	101
Plant and machinery at cost	102
Motor vehicles at cost	103
Fixtures and fittings at cost	104

Current assets

Bank deposit account	201
Bank current account	202
Investments	203
Sales ledger control account (total debtors)	204

Liabilities and expense items

Proprietors' capital	301
Provision for depreciation: land and buildings	310
Provision for depreciation: plant and machinery	311
Purchase ledger control account	320
Wages and salaries	330
Rent and rates	340
Advertising expenses	350
Motor expenses	351
Bank charges	360

Income

Credit sales	400
Cash sales	401
Fees	402
Interest receivable	403

3 Coding systems

3.1 Features of good coding systems

- Ease of use and communication

- Potential for expansion

- Flexibility: small changes in item classification can be incorporated without major changes to the coding system itself.

- A unique reference code for key items, such as customer account number, supplier account number, stock code number or employee number

- Universality: every recorded item can be suitably coded.

- Simplicity.

- The likelihood of errors going undetected should be minimised.

- No duplication.

- A readily available index or reference book of codes.

- Existing codes should be reviewed regularly and out-of-date codes removed.

- Code numbers should be issued from a single, central point. Different people should not be allowed to add new codes to the existing list independently.

3.2 Types of coding systems

Various coding systems (or combinations of them) may be used when designing codes.

Sequence codes. No attempt is made to **classify** the item to be coded. It is simply given the next available number in a rising sequence. New items can only be inserted at the end of the list; thus the codes for similar items may be very different.

For example:

1 = saucepans
2 = kettles
3 = pianos
4 = dusters

Sequence codes are rarely used when a large number of items are involved.

Block codes provide a different sequence for each differing group of items. For example for a particular firm, customers may be divided up according to area:

South East   Code numbers 10,000 - 19,999
South West   Code numbers 20,000 - 29,999
Wales   Code numbers 30,000 - 39,999
and so on

The code is sequential within each block.

Significant digit codes incorporate some digits which are part of the description of the item being coded. An example is:

5000   Electric light bulbs
5025   25 watt
5040   40 watt
5060   60 watt
5100   100 watt
and so on

Where the digits in a code are intended to follow a pattern or structure, but the code numbers themselves are of no significance, the term **faceted code** is sometimes used in preference to significant digit codes. For example, in a costing system, we might have a three-figure code.

Digit	Code	Meaning
First	1	Material cost
	2	Labour cost
	3	Expense
Second	1	Direct production cost
	2	Indirect production cost
	3	Marketing cost
	4	Administration cost
Third	1	Variable cost
	2	Fixed cost
	3	Mixed cost

Code 211 would then indicate a variable direct labour production cost.

Sometimes **mnemonic codes** are used, to help people to recognise the meaning of the code more easily. A mnemonic code uses letters that give some clue to the meaning of the code, for example area codes might be N, S, E, W, SW etc, or clothes sizes S (small), M (medium), L (large). The first letters of a UK postcode are mnemonic (eg BS = Bristol; YO = York) but the remainder of the code is not.

4 Processing data

Both manual and computer data processing can be divided into two broad types.

- Batch processing
- Real time processing

4.1 Batch processing

Batch processing is 'the processing as a group of a number of transactions of a similar kind which have been entered over a period of time to a computer system.' For example the **payroll** work for salaried staff is done in one operation once a month. To help with organising the work, the payroll office might deal with **each department separately**, and do the salaries for department 1, then the salaries for department 2, and then department 3, and so on. If this is the case, then the batch processing would be carried out by dividing the transaction records into smaller batches, one for each department.

Transactions will be collected up over a period of time, perhaps in a transaction file, and will then be dealt with all at the same time. Some delay in processing the transactions must therefore be acceptable. For example, in a payroll system, employees must agree to regular weekly or monthly payment.

Batch input allows for good **control** over the input data, because data can be grouped into **numbered batches**. The batches are dispatched for processing and processed in these batches, and printed output **listings** of the processed transactions are usually organised in batch order.

If any records go missing - for example, in transit - it is possible to locate the batch in which the missing record should belong. **Errors** in transaction records can be located more quickly by identifying its **batch number**. A check can be made to ensure that every batch of data sent off for processing is eventually received back from processing, so that entire batches of records do not go missing.

Bulk volume processing in batch mode allows the **processing** to be divided into separate stages, where each stage of processing is performed by a **separate computer programs**. (Long complex programs are more prone to error and take up more space in the CPU's internal store.)

Example

A company operates a computer based sales ledger. The main stages of processing are as follows.

Step 1. The sales invoices are prepared manually and one copy of each is retained. At the end of the day all the invoices are clipped together and a batch control slip is attached. The sales clerk allocates the next unused batch number in the batch control book. He or she enters the batch number on the control slip, together with the total number of documents and the total value of the invoices. The control details are also entered in the control book.

Step 2. The batch of invoices is then passed to the data processing department. The data control clerk records the batch as having been received.

Step 3. The invoice and control details are encoded, verified, and input to the computer. The first program is a validation program which performs various checks on the data and produces a listing of all valid invoices together with some control totals. It also produces rejection listings (exception reports).

Step 4. The data control clerk reconciles the totals on the batch control slip with the totals for valid and rejected data.

Step 5. The ledger update program is run to process the invoice data.

Step 6. Among the information, the computer prints out the total of invoices posted to the ledger and the data control clerk again reconciles this to the batch totals, before despatching all the output documents to the sales department.

Step 7. All rejected transaction records are carefully investigated and followed up, usually to be re-input with the next processing run.

4.2 Real-time processing

Real-time processing is the continual receiving and rapid processing of data so as to be able, more or less instantly, to feed back the results of that input to the source of the data.

Real-time processing uses an **on-line** computer system (see below) to interrogate or update files as requested rather than batching such requests together for subsequent processing.

Transactions for processing might arise infrequently, and so it would take too long to build up a batch for processing at the same time. Instead, each transaction would be **processed individually as it arises**.

Alternatively, the information user might want to process a transaction immediately, and would not be prepared to accept the delay implicit in batch processing.

As each transaction is processed immediately on input (rather than in batches), all the batch processing stages of input, validation of data, updating and output are applied to that one transaction by a single computer program.

Real time systems are becoming more and more common in modern business. Here are some examples.

    (a) As a sale is made in a department store or a supermarket and details are keyed in on the **point of sale terminal**, the stock records are updated in real-time. Any customer wishing to buy a product can be informed as to whether the item is available or not (if not, an alternative might be offered).

    (b) Although the stock files are maintained in real time, other files (for example sales analysis or debtors) may be batch processed at a later stage with the accumulated sales details from each point of sale terminal.

    (c) In **banking and credit card** systems whereby customer details are maintained in a real-time environment. There can be immediate access to customer balances, credit position and authorisation for withdrawals (or use of a credit card).

    (d) **Travel agents**, **airlines** and **theatre ticket** agencies all have to use real-time systems. Once a hotel room, plane seat or theatre seat is booked, everybody on the system must know about it immediately so that they do not sell the same holiday or seat to two (or more) different customers.

5 Integrated systems and databases

Clearly, you do not want to code or enter data more than once, each time to different systems. For example, it will save time if your purchase order system can be used, on receipt of goods, to update the stock control system.

Systems which connect applications together are called integrated systems.

The systems are distinct but they present a single view to the user.

The diagram below might make all this more clear. It deals with stock control, sales order and purchases applications.

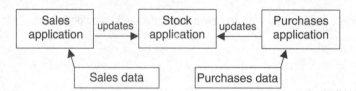

5.1 Integrated systems

Purchase order systems do not necessarily need to be linked up (**integrated**) with other systems. In a very **small business**, for instance, Employee A, who makes the final product, may mention (at tea-break) to Employee B, who is in charge of buying materials, that she is about to run out of Widgets and could Employee B please buy the best Widgets available. Employee B would happen to know that Sterling Supplies was currently offering the best deal on Widgets and place the order accordingly.

In a very **large business,** using millions of different parts and making many different products, this is impractical. For one thing Employee A would not even meet Employee B at tea-break: they may be on different sites. For another, Employee B could not possibly remember off the top of his or her head who the best supplier for a particular component might be, and certainly would not remember their name and address details.

An integrated computerised purchase order system, however, could do two things automatically.

    (a)   Notify the purchase order department that stocks of Widgets were low and fresh supplies were needed
    (b)   Provide the details of suppliers offering the best deal on Widgets

The stock level details would be drawn from a **stock system**, and the best supplier details would be drawn from the stock system via the **accounting system**.

5.2 Database

A **database** is a collection of information organised in such a way that the user can quickly select desired pieces of data. It differs from an integrated system in that all applications use and update a single set of records.

The term **database** is now usually used to describe a **computerised** database which is a sort of electronic filing system, automating many of the manual data storage and retrieval procedures that we have already described.

5.2.1 Structure of a database

Traditional databases are organised by **fields**, **records** and **files**. Each **file** is made up of a number of **records**. Each record is divided into a number of **fields**. We can demonstrate the structure of a database, such as a telephone directory, as follows.

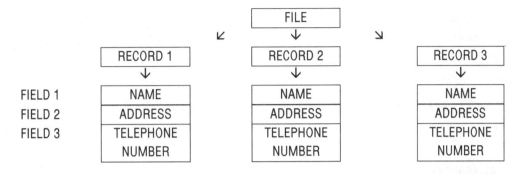

Area within database	Example
File	Telephone directory
Record within file	Entry for each person
Fields within record	Name, address, telephone number

5.2.2 Use

Since a database refers to a **store of information** which can be kept in a manual or electronic system, its main use is to access, sort and retrieve previously stored information **very quickly**.

Probably the most common use is a database of **customer information**. For example, when you use a **loyalty card** at Tesco, Sainsbury or Safeway, information about your buying habits is collected via a computer system, and added to the supermarket's **customer database**. It is later analysed, and you are added to a mailing list of people who are interested in, say, baby food, or beer, or perfume, or whatever your buying behaviour indicates about you.

5.2.3 Advantages of database systems

Advantages of a database system

(a) **Avoidance of unnecessary duplication of data**

It recognises that data can be used for many purposes but **only needs to be input and stored once**. The drawback to single entry input is that one department only must accept responsibility for the accuracy of the input.

(b) **Multi-purpose data**

From (a), it follows that although data is input once, it can be **used for several purposes**.

(c) **Data for the organisation as a whole**

The database concept encourages management to regard data as a **resource that must be properly managed** just as any other resource. The installation of a database system encourages management to analyse data, relationships between data items, and how data is used in different applications.

(d) **Consistency**

Because data is only held once, it is easier to ensure that it is **up-to-date**, so that no department in an organisation uses out-of-date data, or data that differs from the data used by other departments. They should not come to different decisions simply because they were based on different data.

(e) **New uses for old data**

Data on file is **independent of the user programs that access the data**. This allows greater flexibility in the ways that data can be used. New programs can be easily introduced to make use of existing data in a different way.

(f) **New applications**

Developing new application programs with a database system is easier than developing other applications, because **the programmer is not responsible for the file organisation**, which is already taken care of by the database management software.

For example, the sales administration and the marketing departments of an organisation may need customer name and address details. If these two systems operated separate systems, they would both need to input details of any change of address.

If they share a common database for this information, it only needs to be input once, and there is no chance of conflicting versions of the same data arising.

5.2.4 Types of database

Most organisations store vast amounts of data in databases, and in order to organise this data in the most efficient manner, they have different types of database, for example, a customer database. The other types of database that you need to know about are as follows.

- Supplier database
- Sales ledger database
- Stock control database
- Employee database
- Purchase ledger database
- Cash log

5.2.5 Supplier database

Just as a **customer database** stores information relating to the customers of an organisation, a **supplier database** stores information relating to the suppliers of an organisation. Such information might include the following.

- Name, address and telephone number of supplier
- Goods supplied
- Credit terms
- Discounts given
- Supplier reference

We can demonstrate a supplier database further by considering the ways in which you might use such a database at home. Suppose, for example, that you wish to have your house decorated, your first step will probably be to contact a number of decorators and ask them to give you a quote for the job. If you have three such quotes, you will have your own **supplier database**, with information regarding the name, address and telephone number of each decorator (or 'supplier'). Other details held might be whether they are VAT registered (this will obviously affect the amount that you will be charged), whether materials are supplied, credit terms (when payment is due) and how much the final quote for the job is.

5.2.6 Sales ledger database

Sales ledger databases, as the name suggests, provide a collection of information relating to the sales of an organisation. The following information may be stored on a sales ledger database.

(a)   **Invoice number**. Each sale is assigned an invoice number which is used to identify a particular transaction. Such *codes* may be used to categorise sales, for example, an invoice number may be followed by a letter which indicates the area in which the sale was made. Invoices may then be grouped in order to show sales by geographical area.

(b)   **Customer name** and **address**.

(c)   **Customer reference**. For example, an accounts system might use codes to identify customers (and also suppliers), with, say a 5-letter code for each customer (and a 10-digit code for each supplier). The code KJAKE could be used to represent a regular customer, Kevin Jake Ltd of Wiltshire House, Rugby Lane, Cambridge. To process any transaction involving this customer, the computer user could simply specify the code KJAKE in the customer reference code field. Typically, as soon as the code is entered, the name (or name and address) will be displayed on the computer user's VDU screen.

(d)   **Date of transaction**

(e)   **Value of transaction** (both inclusive and exclusive of VAT)

(f)   **Amount of VAT**

(g)   Any **discounts** given.

(h)   **Details of transactions**

5.2.7 Employee database

In very large organisations where there are many employees, information relating to its employees may be held in the personnel department on an **employee database**. Organisations such as hospitals may have thousands of employees, and many of these people may come and go regularly, such as doctors who may only spend six months in any one hospital at a time. It is vital therefore that information relating to employees of large organisations is up-to-date and can be accessed quickly and easily. In order to store and retrieve such information in the most efficient manner, it is a good idea to assign each employee a unique reference code or an **employee number**.

Such a reference may contain information relating to whether the employee is full-time or part-time, the department the employee belongs to, and whether the employee is paid weekly or monthly and so on.

Typical employee information

- Name of employee
- Address and telephone number of employee
- Date of birth
- Details of next of kin
- Joining date
- Pay review date
- Current salary
- Tax code
- Marital status
- Details of any foreign languages spoken

The final point above could be very useful information if a patient who could not understand any English were admitted to hospital in England. The communication problems could be overcome by tracking down a member of staff who was able to speak the required foreign language - and the employee database would house such information.

5.2.8 Stock control database

Stock is often one of the most valuable assets of a company. It is important therefore that the amount and value of stock can be identified at any moment in time.

Most items of stock are assigned a unique code, called a **stock code**. In organisations where large amounts of stock are bought, manufactured, or sold, the chances of selecting the incorrect stock items should be reduced if each item has its own unique reference. Many catalogues, such as those in Argos, assign a code to each of its products to make the process of ordering sales much easier.

Similar stock items may be categorised with ease if part of their code relates to the type of stock that they are. For example, suppose a garden centre assigned a code TT01H to its Tom Thumb fuchsias. The TT01 is the unique code for Tom Thumb fuchsias, and the H is used to signify that such a fuchsia is hardy (as opposed to non-hardy). Winston Churchill fuchsias might be coded WC01N, where the WC01 is the unique code for the Winston Churchill fuchsia, and the 'N' denotes that it is a non-hardy fuchsia. All stock items ending with an 'H' may be categorised as hardy stock, and all stock items ending with an 'N' may be categorised as non-hardy stock.

Information which may be found on a stock control database

- Stock code
- Description of stock item
- Value of stock item
- Number of stock items held
- Supplier of stock item

Answers to activities

Chapter 2

Answer 2.1

(a)

10
<u>17</u>
<u>27</u>

(b)

217
<u>1,420</u>
<u>1,637</u>

(c)

100,000	10,000	1,000	100	10	1
	1	0	7	7	7
2	5	9	3	2	1
2	7	0	0	9	8
	+1	+1			

So the answer is 270,098.

Note: You do not have to use this format. It is there to remind you what the numbers represent and to show the workings.

(d)

10,000,000	1,000,000	100,000	10,000	1,000	100	10	1
	1	5	7	2	6	5	1
1	0	3	2	1	1	2	3
1	1	8	9	3	7	7	4

So the answer is 11,893,774.

Answer 2.2

(a)

10
100
<u>1,000</u>
<u>1,110</u>

(b)

10,000	1,000	100	10	1
	2	7	6	0
	4	3	2	0
	5	1	1	1
1	2	1	9	1
+1	+1			

The answer is 12,191.

(c)

10,000	1,000	100	10	1
	4	7	6	5
	2	2	7	7
	3	5	1	2
1	0	5	5	4
+1	+1	+1	+1	

The answer is 10,554.

(d)

10,000	1,000	100	10	1
	1	2	3	4
1	1	2	3	4
2	2	7	7	7
3	5	2	4	5
	+1	+1	+1	

The answer is 35,245.

(e)

10,000	1,000	100	10	1
	1	2	3	4
	5	6	7	8
	9	1	0	1
	2	4	6	8
	3	5	7	9
2	2	0	6	0
+2	+2	+2	+3	

The answer is 22,060.

Answer 2.3

(a)

```
    17
    10
     7
```

(b)

```
  1,368
    521
    847
```

(c)

1,000,000	100,000	10,000	1,000	100	10	1
1	9	8	7	6	5	4
	8	7	6	5	4	3
1	1	1	1	1	1	1

The answer is 1,111,111.

(d)

100,000,000	10,000,000	1,000,000	100,000	10,000	1,000	100	10	1
2	5	7	7	4	1	9	9	9
1	7	2	5	1	1	3	2	1
0	8	5	2	3	0	6	7	8
−1	+10							

The answer is 85,230,678.

Answer 2.4

(a)

```
    500        or        300        500
    300−                 150+       450−
    200                  450         50
    150−
     50
```

(b)

1,700	*or*	1,300	1,700
1,300–		200+	1,500–
400		1,500	200
200–			
200			

(c)

10,000	*1,000*	*100*	*10*	*1*
1	0	0	0	0
	5	7	6	1
4	2	3	9	
−1	−1 + 10	−1 + 10	−1 + 10	+ 10

	1,000	*100*	*10*	*1*
	4	2	3	9
	3	2	9	9
		9	4	0
	−1	−1 + 10	+ 10	

The answer is 940.

Alternatively add together 5,761 and 3,299 first, then subtract from 10,000.

1,000	*100*	*10*	*1*
5	7	6	1
3	2	9	9
9	0	6	0
+1	+1	+1	

10,000	*1,000*	*100*	*10*	*1*
1	0	0	0	0
	9	0	6	0
		9	4	0
−1	−1 + 10	−1 + 10	+ 10	

Again, the answer is 940.

(d)

1,000	100	10	1
5	0	0	0
1	1	1	1
3	8	8	9
−1	−1 + 10	−1 + 10	+ 10

1,000	100	10	1
3	8	8	9
2	2	2	2
1	6	6	7

The answer is 1,667.

Alternatively add together 1,111 and 2,222 first, then subtract from 5,000.

1,000	100	10	1
1	1	1	1
2	2	2	2
3	3	3	3

1,000	100	10	1
5	0	0	0
3	3	3	3
1	6	6	7
−1	−1 + 10	−1 + 10	+ 10

Again, the answer is 1,667.

(e) You could do the subtraction in three stages, ie 100,000 − 9,762 = 90,238; 90,238 − 12,321 = 77,917 and 77,917 − 25,750 = 52,167.

However, it is quicker to use the alternative method by adding 9,762 + 12,321 + 25,750 and then subtracting the total from 100,000 as follows.

10,000	1,000	100	10	1
	9	7	6	2
1	2	3	2	1
2	5	7	5	0
4	7	8	3	3
+1	+1	+1		

100,000	10,000	1,000	100	10	1
1	0	0	0	0	0
	4	7	8	3	3
	5	2	1	6	7
−1	−1 + 10	−1 + 10	−1 + 10	−1 + 10	+ 10

Again, the answer is 52,167.

Answer 2.5

(a) $12 \times 7 = 84$

If you did not know the multiplication tables, you could multiply 7 by 10 and by 2 and add the results together.

$$7 \times 10 = \quad 70$$
$$7 \times 2 = \quad \underline{14}$$
$$(7 \times 12) \quad \underline{84}$$

(b)

1,000	100	10	1	
	5	2	5	
				× 5
2	6	2	5	
+2	+1	+2		

The answer is 2,625.

(c)

10,000	1,000	100	10	1	
	1	5	2	5	
					× 20
3	0	5	0	0	
+3	+10	+5	+10		

If you were not happy about multiplying by 20, multiply by 2 and then by 10.

$1,525 \times 2 = 3,050$

$3,050 \times 10 = 30,500$

10,000	1,000	100	10	1
	1	5	2	5
				× 7
1	0	6	7	5
+1	+3	+1	+3	

$1,525 \times 20 =$ 30,500
$1,525 \times 7 =$ 10,675
$1,525 \times 27 =$ 41,175

(d)

1,000,000	100,000	10,000	1,000	100	10	1
	1	7	9	3	2	1
						× 5
	8	9	6	6	0	5
	+3	+4	+1	+1		

$896,605 \times 10 = 8,966,060$.

So the answer is 8,966,050.

Answer 2.6

Tutorial note. In all cases, you can make a short cut by choosing which numbers to multiply first.

(a) $5 \times 2 = 10$

$760 \times 10 = 7,600$

The answer is 7,600.

(b) $3 \times 3 = 9$

10,000	1,000	100	10	1
	1	2	7	5
				× 9
1	1	4	7	5
+1	+2	+6	+4	

The answer is 11,475.

(c) $5 \times 7 = 35$

$35 \times 1,000 = 35,000$

The answer is 35,000.

(d)   Did you notice that 25 × 4 = 100?

5,731 × 100 = 573,100.

The answer is 573,100.

Answer 2.7

(a)

100	10	1	
1	6	9	
−1	+10	+30	
0	16	39	÷13
	1	3	

The answer is 13.

(b) $\dfrac{9,639}{9} = 1,071$

1,000	100	10	1	
9	6	3	9	
		+60		
9	0	63	9	÷9
1	0	7	1	

(c) $\dfrac{175,985}{5} = 35,197$

100,000	10,000	1,000	100	10	1	
1	7	5	9	8	5	
−1	+10	+20		+40	+30	
0	17	25	9	48	35	÷5
	3	5	1	9	7	

Answer 2.8

(a)

$$100 - 1 = \qquad 99$$
$$9 \times 7 = \qquad \underline{63} \quad -$$
$$\qquad\qquad\qquad 36$$
$$5 \times 2 = \qquad \underline{10} \quad \times$$
$$\qquad\qquad\qquad \underline{360}$$

Reason

$360 = 36 \times 10$

$5 \times 2 = 10$, so we need 36.

$9 \times 7 = 63$. This leaves us with 100 and 1.

$100 - 1 = 99$

$99 - 63 = 36$

(b)

$$75 \times 8 = \qquad 600$$
$$4 \times 4 = \qquad \underline{16} \quad +$$
$$\qquad\qquad\qquad 616$$
$$3 - 1 = \qquad \underline{2} \quad -$$
$$\qquad\qquad\qquad \underline{614}$$

Reason

Remember that $75 \times 2 = 150$

So $75 \times 4 = 300$

We need 600, so we need $75 \times 4 \times 2$, or 75×8.

This leaves 3, 4, 1, 4 to make 14.

The easiest way is to take:

$4 \times 4 = 16$

Then $3 - 1 = 2$ and subtract to get 14.

(c)

$$25 - 2 = \qquad 23$$
$$\qquad\qquad\qquad \underline{8} \quad \times$$
$$\qquad\qquad\qquad \underline{184}$$

Reason

Remember that $25 \times 4 = 100$

$184 = 200 - 16$

$25 \times 8 = 200$, but how do we get 16?

Remember that $8 \times 2 = 16$, so if we subtract 2 from 25 **before** multiplying by 8, we must get the answer we need.

In other words: $200 - 16 = 8 \times (25 - 2)$

In maths, items in brackets are calculated **before** any other calculations, so $8 \times (25 - 2) = 8 \times 23$.

(d)

$$50 + 2 = \qquad 52$$
$$4 \times 3 = \qquad \underline{12} \quad \times$$
$$\underline{624}$$

Reason

Remember that $50 \times 2 = 100$, so

$$600 \;=\; 50 \times 2 \times 6$$
$$=\; 50 \times 12$$

This leaves 24 to find or 2×12, in other words:

$(50 + 2) \times 12 = 624$

When we look at the numbers available, we have 50 and 2. So we need to find 12 from 6, 3, 1 and 4. The quickest way is $4 \times 3 = 12$.

However you could also have used $3 - 1 = 2 \times 6 = 12$

It is even possible to use all the numbers: $4 - 3 = 1 + 1 = 2 \times 6 = 12$!

Chapter 3

Answer 3.1

(a) $B = 2$, $C = 3$. So $B/C = 2/3$. This means that B is 2/3 the size of C.

(b) $A = 1$, $C = 3$. So $A/C = 1/3$. This means that A is 1/3 the size of C, or that C is 3 times bigger than A.

(c)   The whole circle $= A + B + C$

$$= 1 + 2 + 3$$

$$= 6 \text{ parts}$$

(d) $\dfrac{A}{\text{Total circle}} = \dfrac{1 \text{ part}}{6 \text{ parts}} = \dfrac{1}{6}$

(e) $\dfrac{2}{6} = \dfrac{1}{3}$. Remember to divide top and bottom by 2 to simplify the fraction.

(f) $\frac{3}{6} = \frac{1}{2}$.

(g) $\frac{1}{6} + \frac{1}{3} = \frac{1}{6} + \frac{2}{6}$

$= \frac{1+2}{6}$

$= \frac{3}{6}$

$= \frac{1}{2}$

(h) $\frac{1}{2} + \frac{1}{2} = 1$. This should not surprise you as we effectively added A + B + C.

Answer 3.2

(a) First find the common denominator. Looking at the two lowest denominators: 6 × 4 = 24. As 8 × 3 = 24, we use 24 as the lowest common denominator.

$\frac{3}{8} - \frac{1}{6} + \frac{1}{4} = \frac{9}{24} - \frac{4}{24} + \frac{6}{24} = \frac{9-4+6}{24} = \frac{11}{24}$

(b) As 4 × 2 = 8, the lowest common denominator is 8.

$\frac{7}{8} - \frac{1}{4} - \frac{1}{2} = \frac{7-2-4}{8} = \frac{1}{8}$

(c) Remember that 1 is the same as $\frac{12}{12}$.

$1 - \frac{5}{12} + \frac{7}{12} = \frac{12-5+7}{12} = \frac{14}{12}$

The nominator is larger than the denominator! In this case, we have an answer that is larger than one and so we can rewrite the fraction as:

$\frac{14}{12} = \frac{12+2}{12}$

$= \frac{12}{12} + \frac{2}{12}$

$= 1\frac{2}{12}$

$= 1\frac{1}{6}$

Answer 3.3

$\frac{29}{35}$ = 0.8285714285714

(a)	0.8286	(discarding the 7 adds 1 to the 5)
(b)	0.829	(discarding the 5 adds 1 to the 8)
(c)	0.83	(discarding the 8 adds 1 to the 2)
(d)	0.82857	(discarding the 1 adds nothing to the 7)
(e)	0.8286	(discarding the 7 adds 1 to the 5)
(f)	0.829	(discarding the 5 adds 1 to the 8)

Answer 3.4

10.00 – 7.50 = 2.50

So you have £2.50 left.

$\frac{2.50}{10.00}$ × 100% = 25%

Answer 3.5

$\frac{17}{100}$ × 395 = £67.15

Therefore the discounted price is £395 – £67.15 = £327.85

Tutorial note. You may have realised that the discounted price must be (100% – 17%), ie 83% of the original price. So the discounted price is $\frac{83}{100}$ × 395 = £327.85.

Answer 3.6

The key wording is the mark-up of 20% is **on cost**. This means that cost is 100%, mark-up is 20% and so the selling price is 120%.

Therefore original cost = $\frac{200}{120}$ × 100 = £166.67

Check:

	£
Original cost (100%)	166.67
Mark-up (20%)	33.33
Selling price (120%)	200.00

Answer 3.7

Selling price	100%
Cost	95%
Gross profit	5%

Gross profit is 5% of sales.

So, in this case, cost $= \dfrac{95}{100} \times £200$

$= £190$

Answer 3.8

(a) **Tutorial note**. Just because there are four people rather than two does not mean that the question is more difficult. Calculate the total number of parts. Calculate the value of one part. Then allocate the correct number of parts to each person.

Total number of parts: 6 + 1 + 2 + 3 = 12
Value of one part = £600 ÷ 12 = £50

	£
A = 6 parts = 6 × £50	300
B = 1 part = 1 × £50	50
C = 2 parts = 2 × £50	100
D = 3 parts = 3 × £50	150
	600

(b) Number of parts = 5 + 3 + 2 = 10

One part $= \dfrac{£1,000}{10} = £100$

97

	£
A = 5 parts	500
B = 3 parts	300
C = 2 parts	200
	1,000

(c) Number of parts = 4 + 3 + 3 = 10

One part = $\dfrac{£100}{10}$ = £10

	£
Bob = 4 parts	40
Charlie = 3 parts	30
Dave = 3 parts	30
	100

(d) Number of parts = 2 + 2 + 1 + 1 = 6

One part = $\dfrac{£12,000}{6}$ = £2,000

	£
A = 2 parts	4,000
B = 2 parts	4,000
C = 1 part	2,000
D = 1 part	2,000
	12,000

Answer 3.9

(a) 4 (4 × 4 = 16)

(b) 30

(c) 55

(d) 121

Chapter 4

Answer 4.1

(a) $25 = d \times 100\%$
      $25 = 0.25 \times 100\%$

   so d = 0.25

(b)   p $= 0.75 \times 100\%$
          $= 75\%$

(c)   p $= 0.50 \times 100\%$
          $= 50\%$

Answer 4.2

(a)   x + y = 7
      x = 2

   So   2 + y   =   7   (deduct 2 from both sides)
          y   =   7 − 2
          y   =   5

(b)   x + y = 10
      y = −4

          x − 4   =   10   (add 4 to both sides)
          x   =   10 + 4
          x   =   14

(c)   x + y = 70   (deduct x from both sides)
      y = 70 − x

(d) $\dfrac{x}{y} = 0.75$

      x = 3

          $\dfrac{3}{y}$ =   0.75   (multiply both sides by y)

          3   =   0.75y   (divide both sides by 0.75)

          $\dfrac{3}{0.75}$ =   y   (reverse the sides, so the unknown is on the left)

          y   = $\dfrac{3 \times 4}{3}$ (multiply the nominator and denominator by 4)

          y   = $\dfrac{3 \times 4}{0.75}$

          y   =   4

Answer 4.3

In the last row across, we have

$$\clubsuit + \clubsuit + \spadesuit + \heartsuit = 13$$

We are given that $\clubsuit = 2$ so

$$2 + 2 + \spadesuit + \heartsuit = 13 \qquad \text{(deduct 4 from both sides)}$$
$$\spadesuit + \heartsuit = 9$$

Now look at the second row across.

$$\diamond + \heartsuit + \clubsuit + \spadesuit = 16 \qquad \text{(rewriting the left hand side in a different order)}$$
$$\diamond + \clubsuit + (\spadesuit + \heartsuit) = 16$$
$$\diamond + 2 + 9 = 16 \qquad \text{(deduct 11 from both sides)}$$
$$\diamond = 5$$

In the extreme right hand column down.

$$* + \spadesuit + \diamond + \heartsuit = 22 \qquad \text{(rewriting the left hand side)}$$
$$* + \diamond + (\spadesuit + \heartsuit) = 22$$
$$* + 5 + 9 = 22 \qquad \text{(deduct 14 from both sides)}$$
$$* = 8$$

In the extreme left hand column down.

$$* + \diamond + \heartsuit + \clubsuit = 18$$
$$8 + 5 + \heartsuit + 2 = 18 \qquad \text{(deduct 15 from both sides)}$$
$$\heartsuit = 3$$

We have already worked out that $\spadesuit + \heartsuit = 9$

$$\spadesuit + 3 = 9 \qquad \text{(deduct 3 from both sides)}$$
$$\spadesuit = 6$$

The answer is:

*	$\spadesuit$	$\diamond$	$\heartsuit$	$\clubsuit$
8	6	5	3	2

Check that this is correct by testing that the columns and rows come back to the totals given.

Chapter 5

Answer 5.1

(a)

(i)	£1	£482,365
(ii)	£100	£482,400
(iii)	£1,000	£482,000
(iv)	£10,000	£480,000

(b)

(i)	843.7
(ii)	843.67

Answer 5.2

(a) £20 − £2 = £18

(b) £20 − £8 = £12, to the nearest £1

(c) £20 − £11 = £9, to the nearest £1

(d) £20 − £5 = £15, to the nearest £1

See overleaf for information on other
BPP products and how to order

AAT Order

To BPP Professional Education, Aldine Place, London W12 8AW
Tel: 020 8740 2211. Fax: 020 8740 1184
E-mail: Publishing@bpp.com Web:www.bpp.com

Mr/Mrs/Ms (Full name) _____

Daytime delivery address _____   Postcode _____

Daytime Tel _____   E-mail _____

	5/04 Texts	5/04 Kits	Special offer	8/04 Passcards	Success CDs
FOUNDATION (£14.95 except as indicated)				Foundation	
Units 1 & 2 Receipts and Payments	☐	☐	Foundation Sage Bookeeping and Excel Spreadsheets CD-ROM free if ordering all Foundation Text and Kits, including Units 21 and 22/23 ☐	£6.95 ☐	£14.95 ☐
Unit 3 Ledger Balances and Initial Trial Balance	☐ (Combined Text & Kit)				
Unit 4 Supplying Information for Mgmt Control	☐ (Combined Text & Kit)				
Unit 21 Working with Computers (£9.95)	☐				
Unit 22/23 Healthy Workplace/Personal Effectiveness (£9.95)	☐				
Sage and Excel for Foundation (Workbook with CD-ROM £9.95)	☐				
INTERMEDIATE (£9.95 except as indicated)					
Unit 5 Financial Records and Accounts	☐	☐		£5.95 ☐	£14.95 ☐
Unit 6/7 Costs and Reports (Combined Text £14.95)	☐			£5.95 ☐	
Unit 6 Costs and Revenues		☐			£14.95 ☐
Unit 7 Reports and Returns		☐			
TECHNICIAN (£9.95 except as indicated)					
Unit 8/9 Core Managing Performance and Controlling Resources		☐	Spreadsheets for Technicians CD-ROM free if take Unit 8/9 Text and Kit ☐	£5.95 ☐	£14.95 ☐
Spreadsheets for Technician (Workbook with CD-ROM)	☐				
Unit 10 Core Managing Systems and People (£14.95)	☐ (Combined Text & Kit)			£5.95 ☐	£14.95 ☐
Unit 11 Option Financial Statements (A/c Practice)	☐	☐		£5.95 ☐	
Unit 12 Option Financial Statements (Central Govnmt)	☐	☐		£5.95 ☐	
Unit 15 Option Cash Management and Credit Control	☐	☐		£5.95 ☐	
Unit 17 Option Implementing Audit Procedures	☐ (Combined Text & Kit)			£5.95 ☐	
Unit 18 Option Business Tax FA04 (8/04) (£14.95)	☐ (Combined Text & Kit)			£5.95 ☐	
Unit 19 Option Personal Tax FA04 (8/04) (£14.95)	☐	☐			
TECHNICIAN 2003 (£9.95)					
Unit 18 Option Business Tax FA03 (8/03) Text & Kit	☐	☐			
Unit 19 Option Personal Tax FA03 (8/03) Text & Kit	☐	☐			
SUBTOTAL	£	£	£	£	£

TOTAL FOR PRODUCTS £ _____

POSTAGE & PACKING

Texts/Kits	First	Each extra
UK	£3.00	£3.00
Europe*	£6.00	£4.00
Rest of world	£20.00	£10.00
Passcards		
UK	£2.00	£1.00
Europe*	£3.00	£2.00
Rest of world	£8.00	£8.00
Success CDs		
UK	£2.00	£1.00
Europe*	£3.00	£2.00
Rest of world	£8.00	£8.00

TOTAL FOR POSTAGE & PACKING £ _____
(Max £12 Texts/Kits/Passcards - deliveries in UK)

Grand Total (Cheques to *BPP Professional Education*)

I enclose a cheque for (incl. Postage) £ _____

Or charge to Access/Visa/Switch

Card Number ☐☐☐☐ ☐☐☐☐ ☐☐☐☐ ☐☐☐☐

CV2 No ☐☐☐ last 3 digits on signature strip

Expiry date _____   Start Date _____

Issue Number (Switch Only) ☐☐

Signature _____

We aim to deliver to all UK addresses inside 5 working days; a signature will be required. Orders to all EU addresses should be delivered within 6 working days. All other orders to overseas addresses should be delivered within 8 working days. * Europe includes the Republic of Ireland and the Channel Islands.

See overleaf for information on other
BPP products and how to order

AAT Order

To BPP Professional Education, Aldine Place, London W12 8AW
Tel: 020 8740 2211. Fax: 020 8740 1184
E-mail: Publishing@bpp.com Web: www.bpp.com

Mr/Mrs/Ms (Full name)

Daytime delivery address

Postcode

Daytime Tel _____ E-mail _____

TOTAL FOR PRODUCTS £ [ ]

POSTAGE & PACKING

Texts/Kits	First	Each extra
UK	£3.00	£3.00 £ [ ]
Europe*	£6.00	£4.00 £ [ ]
Rest of world	£20.00	£10.00 £ [ ]
Passcards		
UK	£2.00	£1.00 £ [ ]
Europe*	£3.00	£2.00 £ [ ]
Rest of world	£8.00	£8.00 £ [ ]
Tapes		
UK	£2.00	£1.00 £ [ ]
Europe*	£3.00	£2.00 £ [ ]
Rest of world	£8.00	£8.00 £ [ ]

TOTAL FOR POSTAGE & PACKING £ [ ]
(Max £12 Texts/Kits/Passcards - deliveries in UK)

Grand Total (Cheques to *BPP Professional Education*)
I enclose a cheque for (incl. Postage) £ [ ]
Or charge to Access/Visa/Switch
Card Number [ ][ ][ ][ ]
CV2 No [ ] last 3 digits on signature strip

Expiry date _____ Start Date _____

Issue Number (Switch Only) _____

Signature _____

OTHER MATERIAL FOR AAT STUDENTS

	8/04 Texts	3/03 Text	3/04 Text

FOUNDATION (£5.95)
Basic Maths and English [ ]

INTERMEDIATE (£5.95)
Basic Bookkeeping (for students exempt from Foundation) [ ]

FOR ALL STUDENTS (£5.95)
Building Your Portfolio (old standards) [ ]
Building Your Portfolio (new standards) [ ]
Basic Costing [ ]

AAT PAYROLL

Finance Act 2004 8/04
December 2004 and June 2005 assessments

Special offer Take Text and Kit together £44.95 [ ]
For assessments in 2005 £44.95 [ ]

Finance Act 2003 9/03
June 2004 exams only

Special offer Take Text and Kit together £44.95 [ ]
For assessments in 2004 £44.95 [ ]

LEVEL 2 Text (£29.95) [ ]
LEVEL 2 Kit (£19.95) [ ]
LEVEL 3 Text (£29.95) [ ]
LEVEL 3 Kit (£19.95) [ ]

SUBTOTAL £ [ ]

£ [ ]

We aim to deliver to all UK addresses inside 5 working days; a signature will be required. Orders to all EU addresses should be delivered within 6 working days. All other orders to overseas addresses should be delivered within 8 working days. * Europe includes the Republic of Ireland and the Channel Islands.

Review Form & Free Prize Draw – Basic Maths and English (9/04)

All original review forms from the entire BPP range, completed with genuine comments, will be entered into one of two draws on 31 January 2005 and 31 July 2005. The names on the first four forms picked out on each occasion will be sent a cheque for £50.

Name: _____   Address: _____

_____

_____

How have you used this Workbook?
(Tick one box only)

☐ Home study (book only)

☐ On a course: college _____

☐ With 'correspondence' package

☐ Other _____

Why did you decide to purchase this Workbook? *(Tick one box only)*

☐ Have used BPP Texts in the past

☐ Recommendation by friend/colleague

☐ Recommendation by a lecturer at college

☐ Saw advertising

☐ Other _____

During the past six months do you recall seeing/receiving any of the following?
(Tick as many boxes as are relevant)

☐ Our advertisement in *Accounting Technician* magazine

☐ Our advertisement in *Pass*

☐ Our brochure with a letter through the post

Which (if any) aspects of our advertising do you find useful?
(Tick as many boxes as are relevant)

☐ Prices and publication dates of new editions

☐ Information on Interactive Text content

☐ Facility to order books off-the-page

☐ None of the above

Your ratings, comments and suggestions would be appreciated on the following areas

	Very useful	Useful	Not useful
Introduction	☐	☐	☐
Chapter contents lists	☐	☐	☐
Examples	☐	☐	☐
Activities and answers	☐	☐	☐

	Excellent	Good	Adequate	Poor
Overall opinion of this Workbook	☐	☐	☐	☐

Do you intend to continue using BPP Interactive Texts/Assessment Kits?   ☐ Yes   ☐ No

Please note any further comments and suggestions/errors on the reverse of this page.

The BPP author of this edition can be e-mailed at: janiceross@bpp.com

Please return this form to: Janice Ross, BPP Professional Education, FREEPOST, London, W12 8BR

Review Form & Free Prize Draw (continued)

Please note any further comments and suggestions/errors below

Free Prize Draw Rules

1   Closing date for 31 January 2005 draw is 31 December 2004. Closing date for 31 July 2005 draw is 30 June 2005.

2   Restricted to entries with UK and Eire addresses only. BPP employees, their families and business associates are excluded.

3   No purchase necessary. Entry forms are available upon request from BPP Professional Education. No more than one entry per title, per person. Draw restricted to persons aged 16 and over.

4   Winners will be notified by post and receive their cheques not later than 6 weeks after the relevant draw date.

5   The decision of the promoter in all matters is final and binding. No correspondence will be entered into.